18. *Boy with Pipe*, 1905. Oil on canvas, 39⅜ x 32. Ambassador and Mrs. John Hay Whitney

Picasso

A LOAN EXHIBITION OF HIS PAINTINGS
DRAWINGS · SCULPTURE · CERAMICS · PRINTS
AND ILLUSTRATED BOOKS

January 8 - February 23

PHILADELPHIA MUSEUM OF ART · 1958

Cover reproduction: *Courtesy of Art News*

98. THREE MUSICIANS, 1921

    Philadelphia Museum of Art

    Gallatin Collection

Still Life with Coffee Pot, 1948
Ceramic plaque. Lent by the artist
(Ceramic catalogue No. 2)

Table of Contents

Ceramic Plates (Ceramic catalogue Nos. 15, 16)
are reproduced on end papers

Lenders to the Exhibition

Larry Aldrich, New York
Mr. and Mrs. Walter Bareiss,
    Greenwich, Connecticut
Heinz Berggruen, Paris
Ivan L. Best, Seattle
Mr. and Mrs. Leigh B. Block, Chicago
Mr. and Mrs. Harry Lynde Bradley, Milwaukee
Edward A. Bragaline, New York
Mr. and Mrs. William A. M. Burden, New York
Mrs. Meric Callery, New York
Mrs. Eleanor Rixson Cannon, New York
Mrs. Gilbert W. Chapman, New York
Walter P. Chrysler, Jr., New York
Stephen C. Clark, New York
Mr. and Mrs. Henry Clifford,
    Radnor, Pennsylvania
Mr. and Mrs. Ralph F. Colin, New York
Mme Marie Cuttoli, Paris
Mr. and Mrs. Richard S. Davis,
    Wayzata, Minnesota
Mr. and Mrs. Rodolphe M. de Schauensee,
    Devon, Pennsylvania
Colonel Valdemar Ebbesen, Oslo
Mrs. Ingeborg Pudelko Eichmann, Florence
Mr. and Mrs. Victor W. Ganz, New York
Mr. and Mrs. Gerald Gidwitz,
    Highland Park, Illinois
Philip L. Goodwin, New York
Guennol Collection, New York
Mr. and Mrs. Ira Haupt, New York

Herbert Hemphill, Jr., New York
Mr. and Mrs. Alex L. Hillman, New York
Joseph H. Hirshhorn, New York
Miss Clara Hoover, New York
Mr. and Mrs. R. Sturgis Ingersoll,
    Penllyn, Pennsylvania
Mr. and Mrs. William B. Jaffe, New York
Mr. and Mrs. Sidney Janis, New York
Sebastián Junyer Vidal, Barcelona
Sylvester W. Labrot, Jr., Hobe Sound, Florida
André Lefèvre, Paris
Mrs. List-Israel, New York
Mrs. H. Gates Lloyd, Haverford, Pennsylvania
Henry P. McIlhenny, Philadelphia
Mlle Dora Maar, Paris
Mr. and Mrs. Arnold H. Maremont, Chicago
Florene and Samuel Marx, Chicago
Mr. and Mrs. Wilbur D. May, Reno
Mr. and Mrs. Morton G. Neumann, Chicago
Clifford Odets, Beverly Hills, California
Mrs. Culver Orswell,
    Pomfret Center, Connecticut
Mr. and Mrs. William S. Paley, New York
Mr. and Mrs. Roland Penrose, London
Pablo Picasso, Cannes
Nelson A. Rockefeller, New York
Dr. and Mrs. Israel Rosen, Baltimore
Siegfried Rosengart, Lucerne
Herbert and Nannette Rothschild, New York
Mr. and Mrs. Daniel Saidenberg, New York

Dance by the Sea, 1933. Lent by Mrs. John Wintersteen (not listed in the catalogue)

PICASSO

Dish with Landscape, 1953
(Ceramic catalogue No. 25)

$\mathcal{P}$reface

The main body of this exhibition of Picasso's works, namely the paintings, sculpture and drawings, was formed by Mr. Alfred Barr and the Museum of Modern Art in New York. Except for minor changes, the same exhibition was seen at the Art Institute of Chicago. The Philadelphia exhibition includes virtually everything seen in New York and Chicago. The generosity of the many lenders was such that only ten pictures were withdrawn and as a like number have been borrowed from other lenders to take their place, the size and substance of the exhibition remains the same.

But in Philadelphia, to illustrate even more thoroughly the prestige and genius of Picasso's accomplishments, it was felt that an even more complete showing of the various media in which the artist has worked would be of great interest to the public. Accordingly, a hundred and thirty prints and a group of posters have been added to the exhibition, covering the graphic work of all his periods. A second feature is the showing, with the prints, of a large collection of nearly all the books that he has ever illustrated.

And to enrich the selection of sculpture already contained in the exhibition, a group of seventy-five examples of ceramics has been borrowed. This large collection of pottery sculpture could form a separate exhibition and indeed was so shown in London and in Rotterdam during the summer of 1957. All the objects were chosen by Picasso himself, two-thirds of them coming from his own private collection and never previously exhibited anywhere. It is thus, I think, the first showing of such a large number of Picasso ceramics in America.

This exhibition was originally planned to show the later works of Picasso, from his *Guernica* mural of 1937 through to the present day. This focus on newer and less known works would have been supremely interesting for all who know Picasso's beginnings. But for the younger generation of art students it was thought wiser to survey the painter's earlier works as well. Hence examples of his entire career of sixty years are now shown. While many of the earlier canvases in this exhibition are so well known they now seem like old masters, there are also a large number of pictures of all periods never before seen in America.

The classic Blue and Pink periods are generously illustrated by many examples showing the depth and tenderness felt by Picasso in his earliest years. However, in considering this part of the exhibition as a whole, one should bear in mind its great culminating picture, *The Saltimbanques* in the Chester Dale Collection, now at the National Gallery in Washington and unfortunately not available for this exhibition. The paintings of the so-called Negro period, which follows immediately, are summed up in the large *Demoiselles d'Avignon* (Cat. 39), which in its day shook the world of art.

The development of Cubism in the years 1908 and 1909, followed by its high period, 1909-1914, is richly shown with numerous paintings that demonstrate its growth and full flowering. Invention follows upon invention, while exploration and discovery, slackened necessarily by the war years, bring us to 1921 and the *Three Musicians*. Both versions (Cat. 98, 99) are shown here together, thus making it possible to assess their diversity as well as their relative values. These two pictures can be considered the apex of thirteen years of Cubism. Simultaneously, following a visit to Rome with the Russian Ballet, Picasso was developing a contrapuntal neo-Classic theme, which was resolved in the same year, 1921, by his painting of *Three Women at the Spring* (Cat. 99a).

From now on he revels in a variety of styles, interweaving them with skillful manipulation and calling up forms as necessity demands, now Cubist, now Classic, the whole oeuvre being shot through with his interest in expressing the new themes of time and space. Outstanding examples of this are *By the Sea*, 1920 (Cat. 90), *Three Dancers*, 1925 (Cat. 110), and *Bather Playing Ball*, 1932 (Cat. 129). For the next few years, preoccupation with bulls and minotaurs becomes a constantly recurring theme, attaining its climax in the Spanish War mural, *Guernica*, 1937 (Cat. 188) where the shrieks of the victims on the canvas still pierce our hearts though the bombers that were its genesis are silent.

The period from *Guernica* to the present shows Picasso in a more personal mood, portraying family and friends and his immediate surroundings. We have portraits of Dora Maar, his brilliant model for so many canvases; of his daughter Maïa; and a long series of his two children, Claude and Paloma, together with their mother, Françoise Gilot. All these reveal Picasso increasingly interested in his family life. The intense happiness caused by the birth of a son in 1946 is vividly portrayed in a suite of pastoral scenes. Here nymphs and fauns, charmed by a shepherd and his pipes, make this episode one of the most delightful in his entire career, reminiscent of the calm of the Rose period emerging from the sorrowful Blue.

All these paintings together with the sculpture and the graphic work suggest Picasso surely as one of the most extraordinary and powerful personalities of the 20th century. His vitality is enormous, his charm incredibly disarming, his invention prodigious, his feats unequalled by any of his contemporaries. Genius or magician? Painter or innovator? As with Leonardo da Vinci and Cézanne, only later generations can be sure. As for me, if I had to risk committing myself on the spot, I already know what I should answer.

Mr. Alfred Barr in his original catalogue for the New York and Chicago showing of this exhibition has already enumerated and thanked on behalf of the Trustees of the Museum of Modern Art, the Art Institute of Chicago and the Philadelphia Museum of Art, the many people who helped him in his great task. We can only endorse this most heartily and add renewed expressions of gratitude, very particularly to the many generous lenders who have so patiently allowed their paintings and sculpture to be away from them for this extended period.

We should like, however, to thank again M. Pablo Picasso for lending his *Guernica* and so many other paintings to the exhibition and in the case of Philadelphia, for his kind gesture in sending also the large group of ceramics from his collection. His interest and support give authority to this great undertaking.

My warmest personal thanks are due to Mr. Alfred Barr, who together with Mr. Monroe Wheeler and Mr. William S. Lieberman at the Museum of Modern Art, has been most helpful in having the many loans extended for inclusion in Philadelphia.

I am deeply grateful to Mr. Douglas Cooper for his indefatigable efforts and extreme kindness in arranging for the inclusion of the ceramic section. It was due to his labor and enthusiasm that the exhibition was originally made. For his knowledge and help I owe my most heartfelt thanks.

At the Museum Boymans in Rotterdam, I wish to thank the director, Dr. Ebbinge Wubben, also the Curator of Modern Art, Dr. J. C. Heyligers, who helped form the ceramic group and oversaw its magnificent installation in their museum. Thanks are also due Mr. Philip James of the Arts Council of Great Britain, under whose auspices the Picasso ceramics were originally shown in England.

To Mr. Louis E. Stern, one of the Board of Governors of the Philadelphia Museum, goes our gratitude for lending his entire collection of illustrated books as well as for his unflagging enthusiasm.

I wish also to thank the many people at the Philadelphia Museum of Art who have worked so assiduously and so long to make this large undertaking possible at all: especially Mr. Henri Marceau, Director, for his shepherding of the entire undertaking and Mr. Carl Zigrosser, Vice-Director, who has made the large selection of prints and who has also written a note on them which follows. The compilation and composition of the Philadelphia edition of the Catalogue has fallen almost entirely upon Mr. Horace H. F. Jayne, Vice-Director, and Miss Barbara Sweeny, Associate Curator of the Johnson Collection, who have earned the gratitude of the Philadelphia Museum, to which I add my own warmest thanks. Mr. Kneeland McNulty has rendered invaluable service in helping to prepare the sections on prints and books, and I am most grateful also to Mr. Louis C. Madeira, Miss Marjorie Lyons, and Miss Jane O'Brien for their contributions to this undertaking. Work for such a large exhibition necessarily falls on every department of the Museum and all members of the staff have applied themselves wholeheartedly to insure its success.

Henry Clifford

Cock, 1932. Bronze, H. 25½. Mr. and Mrs. William A. M. Burden (Sculpture catalogue No. 14)

PICASSO AS A GRAPHIC ARTIST

No estimate of Picasso as an artist is complete without some consideration of his contribution to printmaking, both in books and in separate form. Drawing and design and the urge to communicate are the basic elements of the graphic arts, and these are talents which he, like Goya and Rembrandt, possesses in the highest degree. Picasso is a born printmaker. His complete oeuvre to date—and he has suffered no diminution of creative energy on account of age, nor has he retired—has reached a truly astounding total, well over a thousand prints. It would, of course, be impossible for the Museum to show so great a number, but the selection here shown is, we believe, representative in its quality and variety. Most of the masterpieces are here, from the *Frugal Repast* and Saltimbanques of the Blue Period, the *Salomé*, the Cubist *Still Life with Bottle*, the Sculptor's Studio series from the Vollard Suite, as well as the Minotaur and Blind Minotaur sets leading up to the great *Minotauromachia*, the bitter *Dream and Lie of Franco* and the frenzied *Dancer with Tambourine*. In 1945 Picasso began his association with the lithographic printer Mourlot, a collaboration which has produced many important works, the numerous and varied Heads, the variations on the theme of the Bull, the echoes of sunny Provence in his prints of Pan and Fauns and Centaurs, the large birds and animals, the *Bullfight Game* and *Dance of the Banderillas* in the spirit of the *Verve* drawings of 1953, the later color lithographs, including *The Little Artist* and *Two Clowns*.

As an illustrator of books Picasso is not at all subservient to the text. His illustration is more in the nature of a collaboration, in which the original text is the springboard for the artist's fancy. The prints he has made for books—and only those which contain original prints are displayed here—are thus to be considered as another facet of Picasso's creative endeavor and not at all as a species of literary interpretation. But he has a genuine feeling for typography; and, considered purely as book decoration, his contribution is masterly. Noteworthy among the books are the *St. Matorel* (in Cubist style), the *Chef d'Oeuvre Inconnu*, the lyrically classical *Métamorphoses*, the unique *Histoire Naturelle* (in sugar-lift aquatint), the *Gongora, Chante des Morts, Corps Perdus, De Memoire d'Homme*, and the extraordinary works made in association with that most precious and experimental of typographers, Iliazd (Ilya Zdanevitch): *Afat, Escrito, La Maigre, Chevaux de Minuit*. Special mention should be made of *Poèmes et Lithographies*, not really a book but a collection of original lithographs with pictures and manuscript text by Picasso. This most important document might be called a pictorial recapitulation of his various styles, set in the framework of a stream-of-consciousness commentary, which may or may not bear any relation to the pictures in question.

What is most striking about Picasso is his creative drive and his universality, both in theme and in execution. He has qualities of genius in the field of visual art such as Mozart, for example, displayed in the field of music—a rare combination of seemingly effortless technical mastery and inexhaustible invention. He has rung all the changes in the problem of representation from complete realism to every kind and degree of abstraction. No matter how many liberties he takes in his distortions, he endows all his lines and forms with compelling life. It is characteristic of his exuberant imagination that it often takes the form of variations on a theme —again the analogy with music: he plays with a theme, stressing sometimes one, sometimes another element. No artist has more fully realized the potentialities of such graphic media as etching, engraving, aquatint and lithography. But he is not an artist whose sole motivation is aesthetic: he has human feelings and they find expression in his art. His sympathy for the underdog, his reaction to the cruelty and destruction of war, his tribute to the beauty of woman, to the joy of life, to Pan and the elemental forces of Nature, his probing into the dark Chthonian forces of the subconscious, into the enigma of man and woman and their relation, into the bare essence of mankind from childhood to old age — all these and more give depth and dignity to his art. It is not strange, therefore, that Picasso with his protean aesthetic mastery and humane impulses, looms as a major influence upon the younger generation and upon modern art in general. Picasso is supposed to have said—*la jeunesse, c'est moi.*

CARL ZIGROSSER

The Concierge, 1904. Pen on chine collé, 7 x 11. Philadelphia Museum of Art.
(not listed in the catalogue)

White Table, 1920. Gouache, 10½ x 8⅛.
Mrs. John Wintersteen (not listed in the catalogue)

Catalogue

of the Paintings and Drawings

CATALOGUE OF PAINTINGS AND DRAWINGS

Measurements in inches, height precedes width.
Dated indicates information by the artist's hand.

1. REDEMPTION. c. 1898
Watercolor and conté crayon, 17¾ x 11½
Mr. and Mrs. Justin K. Thannhauser, New York

2. THE ARTIST'S SISTER. Barcelona, 1899
Oil on canvas, 59 x 39½
The artist

3. PAGE OF STUDIES (Heads and Figures).
Paris, 1900
Conté crayon, 5⅛ x 8¼
Ivan L. Best, Seattle

4. LE MOULIN DE LA GALETTE. Paris, autumn 1900
Oil on canvas, 35¼ x 45¾
Mr. and Mrs. Justin K. Thannhauser, New York

5. SELF PORTRAIT. 1901
Oil on cardboard mounted on wood, 20¼ x 12½
Ambassador and Mrs. John Hay Whitney, London

6. WOMAN'S HEAD. Paris, 1901
Oil on millboard, 18½ x 12
Philadelphia Museum of Art, bequest of Lisa
Norris Elkins

7. SELF PORTRAIT. 1901
Oil on canvas, 29 x 23¼
Private collection, New York

8. WOMAN IN BLUE. c. 1901
Oil on canvas, 52⅝ x 39¾
Museo Nacional de Arte Moderno, Madrid

9. DWARF DANCER (La Nana). Paris, 1901
Oil on canvas, 41⅝ x 23¾
Museo de Arte Moderno, Barcelona

10. HARLEQUIN PROPPED ON ELBOW.
Paris, *dated* 1901
Oil on canvas, 33 x 24¾
Mr. and Mrs. Henry Clifford, Radnor, Pa.

11. SEBASTIÁN JUNYER VIDAL. Barcelona,
dated June 1903. Oil on canvas, 49⅜ x 36
Sebastián Junyer Vidal, Barcelona

12. BLIND MAN'S MEAL. Barcelona, 1903
Oil on canvas, 37½ x 37¼
Metropolitan Museum of Art, gift of Mr. and
Mrs. Ira Haupt

13. BROODING WOMAN. Paris, 1904
Watercolor, 10⅝ x 14½
Museum of Modern Art, gift of Mr. and Mrs.
Werner E. Josten

14. WOMAN WITH CHIGNON (Head of the Acrobat's
Wife) Paris, *dated* 1904
Gouache, 16⅞ x 12¼
Art Institute of Chicago, Kate L. Brewster
Bequest

15. WOMAN WITH CROW. Paris, *dated* 1904
Gouache and pastel, 25½ x 19½
Toledo Museum of Art, gift of Edward
Drummond Libbey

16. MEDITATION. Paris, 1904
Watercolor, 13¾ x 10⅛
Mrs. Louise Smith, New York

17. STUDY FOR "THE ACTOR" WITH PROFILES OF
FERNANDE. Paris, winter 1904-05
Pencil, 18½ x 12⅜ (sight)
Nelson A. Rockefeller, New York

18. BOY WITH PIPE. Paris, 1905
Oil on canvas, 39⅜ x 32
Ambassador and Mrs. John Hay Whitney, London

19. BOY ON A HORSE. (Study for "The Watering
Place"). Paris, 1905
Charcoal, 18⅜ x 12
Mr. and Mrs. John W. Warrington, Cincinnati

20. BOY WITH BOUQUET. Paris, 1905
Gouache, 25½ x 21⅜
Mrs. John Wintersteen, Philadelphia

21. PAGE OF STUDIES (Figures and Bulls).
Paris, 1905
Pen and ink, 12¾ x 9¾
Nelson A. Rockefeller, New York

22. MAN'S HEAD. Gosol, 1905
Watercolor, 16 x 13¾
Mr. and Mrs. Rodolphe M. de Schauensee,
Devon, Pennsylvania

23. BOY LEADING A HORSE. Paris, 1905
Oil on canvas, 87 x 51¼
Mr. and Mrs. William S. Paley, New York

24. CIRCUS FAMILY. Paris, 1905
Watercolor and pen, 9½ x 12
Baltimore Museum of Art, Cone Collection

25. MONKEY. Paris, 1905
Watercolor and pen, 19¾ x 12⅝
Baltimore Museum of Art, Cone Collection

26. WOMAN WITH LOAVES. Gosol, 1906 (mistakenly dated 1905)
Oil on canvas, 39 x 27½
Philadelphia Museum of Art, gift of Charles E. Ingersoll

27. LEO STEIN. Paris, 1906
Gouache, 9¾ x 6¾
Baltimore Museum of Art, Cone Collection

28. TWO NUDES. Paris, late 1906
Oil on canvas, 59¾ x 36⅝
G. David Thompson, Pittsburgh

29. PEASANTS FROM ANDORRA. Gosol, summer 1906
Ink, 27⅞ x 16½ (sight)
Art Institute of Chicago, gift of Robert Allerton

30. TWO WOMEN. Paris, late 1906
Charcoal, 24¾ x 18½
Mr. and Mrs. Richard S. Davis, Wayzata, Minnesota

31. TWO NUDES. Paris, late 1906
Pencil and estompe, 24¾ x 18½
Art Institute of Chicago, gift of Mrs. Potter Palmer

32. WOMAN COMBING HER HAIR. Paris, 1906
Oil on canvas, 49¾ x 35½
Florene and Samuel Marx, Chicago

33. LANDSCAPE. Gosol, summer 1906
Oil on canvas, 27½ x 39
Mr. and Mrs. Nate B. Spingold, New York

34. THE BLIND FLOWER VENDOR. 1906
Ink and watercolor, 25 x 18¾
Mr. and Mrs. S. J. Zacks, Toronto

35. WOMAN SEATED AND WOMAN STANDING.
Paris, late 1906
Charcoal, 24⅛ x 18¼
Philadelphia Museum of Art, Arensberg Collection

36. GERTRUDE STEIN. Paris, 1906
Oil on canvas, 39⅜ x 32
Metropolitan Museum of Art, Gertrude Stein Bequest

37. STUDY FOR "LES DEMOISELLES D'AVIGNON."
Paris, dated 1907
Charcoal and pastel, 18⅞ x 25
The artist

38. STUDY FOR "LES DEMOISELLES D'AVIGNON."
Paris, dated 1907
Watercolor, 6¾ x 8¾
Philadelphia Museum of Art, Gallatin Collection

39. "LES DEMOISELLES D'AVIGNON."
Paris, spring 1907. Oil on canvas, 96 x 92
Museum of Modern Art, acquired through the Lillie P. Bliss Bequest

40. HARVESTERS. Paris, spring 1907
Oil on canvas, 25⅝ x 31⅞
Nelson A. Rockefeller, New York

41. SELF PORTRAIT. Paris, dated 1906
Oil on canvas, 36½ x 28¾
Philadelphia Museum of Art, Gallatin Collection

42. FLOWERS. Paris, summer 1907
Oil on canvas, 36½ x 28½
Mr. and Mrs. Ralph F. Colin, New York

43. JUG AND BOWL. Paris, 1907 (presented to Matisse 1907-08)
Oil on wood, 24½ x 19
Private collection, New York

43 a. GRAND DANCER OF AVIGNON. Paris, summer 1907
Oil on canvas, 59 x 39½
Walter P. Chrysler, Jr., New York

44. BATHERS IN THE FOREST. Paris, dated 1908
Watercolor, 19⅛ x 23¾
Mrs. Eleanor Rixson Cannon, New York

45. WOMAN SLEEPING. Paris, spring 1908
Oil on canvas, 32 x 25½
André Lefèvre, Paris

46. SEATED WOMAN. Paris, early 1908
Oil on canvas, 28¾ x 23½
Larry Aldrich, New York

47. KNEELING FIGURE (study for a figure composition). Paris, 1908
Charcoal, 24⅜ x 18½
Nelson A. Rockefeller, New York

48. WOMAN'S HEAD. Paris, spring 1909
Black crayon and gouache, 24¼ x 18¾
Art Institute of Chicago, Charles L. Hutchinson Memorial (Edward E. Ayer Fund)

49. WOMAN WITH PEARS. Horta de San Juan, summer 1909
Oil on canvas, 36 x 28¾
Florene and Samuel Marx, Chicago

50. FEMALE NUDE. Paris, *dated* 1910
Pen and ink and watercolor, 29⅛ x 18⅜
Mr. and Mrs. Richard S. Davis, Wayzata, Minnesota

51. NUDE. Paris, spring 1910
Charcoal, 19⅛ x 12¼
Metropolitan Museum of Art, Alfred Stieglitz Collection

52. GIRL WITH MANDOLIN (Fanny Tellier). Paris, *dated* 1910
Oil on canvas, 39½ x 29
Nelson A. Rockefeller, New York

53. WILHELM UHDE. Paris, spring 1910
Oil on canvas, 32 x 23¾
Mr. and Mrs. Roland Penrose, London

54. D. H. KAHNWEILER. Paris, autumn 1910
Oil on canvas, 39⅝ x 28⅝
Art Institute of Chicago, gift of Mrs. Gilbert W. Chapman

55. FEMALE NUDE. Paris, late 1910
Oil on canvas, 38¾ x 30⅜
Philadelphia Museum of Art, Arensberg Collection

56. "LE TORERO." Céret, summer 1911
Oil on canvas, 18¼ x 15
Nelson A. Rockefeller, New York

57. MAN WITH PIPE. Céret, summer 1911
Ink wash with charcoal, probably oil, 25 x 18¼
Fogg Art Museum, Harvard University

57 a. "L'INDEPENDANT." Céret, summer 1911.
Oil on canvas, 24 x 19¾
Mr. and Mrs. Henry Clifford, Radnor, Pa.

58. "MA JOLIE" (Woman with Zither or Guitar). Paris, winter 1911-12
Oil on canvas, 39⅜ x 25¾
Museum of Modern Art, acquired through the Lillie P. Bliss Bequest

59. BOTTLE OF "VIEUX MARC," GLASS, NEWSPAPER. Céret, spring 1912
Charcoal and pasted papers, 24⅝ x 18½
Mme Marie Cuttoli, Paris

60. STILL LIFE WITH CHAIR CANING. Paris, winter 1911-12
Oil, pasted oilcloth simulating chair caning on canvas, 10⅝ x 13¾ (oval)
The artist

61. AFICIONADO (Bullfight Fan). Sorgues, *dated* 1912
Oil on canvas, 53¼ x 32½
Kunstmuseum, Basle

62. MAN WITH PIPE. 1912
Charcoal, 24½ x 18½
Dr. and Mrs. Israel Rosen, Baltimore

63. MAN WITH GUITAR. Sorgues, *dated* 1912, completed in Paris, spring 1913
Oil on canvas, 51⅞ x 35
Philadelphia Museum of Art, Arensberg Collection

64. GUITAR. Sorgues, summer 1912
Oil on canvas, 28½ x 23⅝ (oval)
Nasjonalgalleriet, Oslo

65. MAN'S HEAD. Paris, winter 1912-13
Charcoal, 24½ x 18⅝
Private collection, New York

66. MAN WITH VIOLIN. Paris, winter 1912-13
Charcoal and pasted papers, 48⅝ x 18⅛
G. David Thompson, Pittsburgh

67. STILL LIFE (Bottle and Glass). Paris, winter 1912-13
Charcoal, ink and pasted paper, 24⅞ x 19⅛
Metropolitan Museum of Art, Alfred Stieglitz Collection

68. VIOLIN AND FRUIT. Paris, 1913
Charcoal and pasted papers, 25½ x 19½
Philadelphia Museum of Art, Gallatin Collection

69. VIOLIN AND GUITAR. Paris, *dated* 1913
Pasted cloth, oil, pencil and plaster on canvas, 36 x 25 (oval)
Philadelphia Museum of Art, Arensberg Collection

70. GUITAR. Spring 1913
Charcoal and pasted papers, 24½ x 18½
Nelson A. Rockefeller, New York

71. BIRD. Late 1913
Oil on canvas, 13 x 5⅞
Private collection, New York

71 a. WOMAN IN ARMCHAIR. Paris, *dated* 1913
Oil on canvas, 59¼ x 39⅜
Mrs. Ingeborg Pudelko Eichmann, Florence

72. CARD PLAYER. Paris, winter 1913-14
Oil on canvas, 42½ x 35¼
Museum of Modern Art, acquired through the
Lillie P. Bliss Bequest

73. HEAD. Paris, c. 1914
Charcoal and pasted papers on cardboard,
17⅛ x 13⅛
Mr. and Mrs. Roland Penrose, London

74. STILL LIFE WITH CALLING CARD. Paris, 1914
Pencil and pasted papers, 5½ x 8¼
Mrs. Gilbert W. Chapman, New York

75. PIPE, GLASS, BOTTLE OF RUM. Paris, 1914
Pencil, gouache and pasted papers on cardboard,
15¾ x 20¾
Museum of Modern Art, gift of Mr. and Mrs.
Daniel Saidenberg

76. AMBROISE VOLLARD. Paris, dated August 1915
Pencil, 18⅜ x 12½
Metropolitan Museum of Art, Whittelsey Fund

77. HARLEQUIN. Paris, dated 1915
Oil on canvas, 72¼ x 41⅜
Museum of Modern Art, acquired through the
Lillie P. Bliss Bequest

78. HEAD OF A YOUNG MAN. Paris, dated 1915
Oil on wood, 10 x 7¼
Mrs. Louise Smith, New York

79. MAN WITH PIPE. Paris, c. 1915
Oil on canvas, 51¼ x 35¼
Art Institute of Chicago, gift of Mary L. Block
in memory of Albert D. Lasker

80. BATHERS. Biarritz, dated 1918
Pencil, 9⅛ x 12¼
Fogg Art Museum, Harvard University,
Cambridge, Meta and Paul J. Sachs Collection

81. PIERROT AND HARLEQUIN. Paris, dated 1918
Pencil, 10¼ x 7½
Art Institute of Chicago, given in memory of
Charles B. Goodspeed by Mrs. Gilbert W.
Chapman

82. FISHERMAN. Probably Biarritz, dated 1918
Pencil, 13¾ x 10
Private collection, New York

83. SLEEPING PEASANTS. Paris, dated 1919
Gouache, 12¼ x 19¼
Museum of Modern Art, Mrs. John D.
Rockefeller, Jr., Fund

84. THREE BALLERINAS. Paris, 1919
Pencil and charcoal, 23⅛ x 17⅜
The artist

85. DIAGHILEV AND SELISBURG, 1919
Pencil, 24⅞ x 18⅞
The artist

86. PEASANT BRIDE AND GROOM. Paris, dated 191?
Conté crayon, 23½ x 18¼
Santa Barbara Museum of Art,
gift of Wright S. Ludington

87. TWO BALLET DANCERS. London, summer 191?
Pencil, 12¼ x 9¼
Mr. and Mrs. Victor W. Ganz, New York

88. PAGE OF SKETCHES. 1919
Pencil, 12½ x 8⅝
Mrs. Culver Orswell, Pomfret Center, Connecticut

89. LANDSCAPE. Juan-les-Pins, 1920
Oil on canvas, 20½ x 27½
The artist

90. BY THE SEA. Juan-les-Pins, summer 1920
(dated by error 1923)
Oil on wood, 32 x 39½
G. David Thompson, Pittsburgh

91. THE RAPE. Dated 1920.
Tempera on wood, 9⅜ x 12⅞
Philip L. Goodwin, New York

92. PIERROT AND HARLEQUIN. Juan-les-Pins,
summer 1920
Gouache, 10⅛ x 7¾
Mrs. Gilbert W. Chapman, New York

93. NESSUS AND DEJANIRA. Juan-les-Pins,
dated 12 September 1920
Pencil, 8¼ x 10¼
Museum of Modern Art, acquired through the
Lillie P. Bliss Bequest

94. NESSUS AND DEJANIRA WITH A SATYR.
Juan-les-Pins, dated 12 September 1920
Watercolor, 8½ x 11¼
Private collection, New York

95. NESSUS AND DEJANIRA. Juan-les-Pins,
dated 22 September 1920
Silverpoint, 8¾ x 10⅝
Nelson A. Rockefeller, New York

96. NUDE SEATED ON A ROCK. 1921
Tempera on wood, 6¼ x 4⅜
Mr. and Mrs. James Thrall Soby, New Canaan,
Connecticut

97. STUDY OF A HAND. Paris, *dated* 20 January 1921
Pastel, 8⅛ x 12½
Nelson A. Rockefeller, New York

98. THREE MUSICIANS. Fontainebleau, *dated* 1921
Oil on canvas, 80 x 74
Philadelphia Museum of Art, Gallatin Collection

99. THREE MUSICIANS. Fontainebleau, *dated* 1921
Oil on canvas, 79 x 87¾
Museum of Modern Art, Mrs. Simon Guggenheim
Fund

99 a. THREE WOMEN AT THE SPRING. *Dated* 1921
Oil on canvas, 80¼ x 68½
Museum of Modern Art,
gift of Mr. and Mrs. Allan D. Emil

100. MOTHER AND CHILD. *Dated* 1921
Oil on canvas, 56½ x 64
Art Institute of Chicago

101. THE RACE. Paris, 1922
Tempera on wood, 12⅞ x 16¼
The artist

102. STANDING NUDE. Dinard, *dated* 1922
Oil on wood, 7½ x 5½
Wadsworth Atheneum, Hartford

103. MANDOLIN ON TABLE. Paris, *dated* 1922
Oil on canvas, 32½ x 39⅜
Mr. and Mrs. William B. Jaffe, New York

104. DR. CLARIBEL CONE. *Dated* 14 July 1922
Pencil, 24¾ x 19¼
Baltimore Museum of Art, Cone Collection

105. ST. SERVAN, NEAR DINARD. 1922
Pencil, 16⅛ x 11⅛ (sight)
Mr. and Mrs. Justin K. Thannhauser, New York

106. STANDING NUDE. *Dated* 1922
Oil on canvas, 10¼ x 8½
Private collection, New York

107. ACTOR IN GREEN. *Dated* 1922
Gouache on paper, 6⅜ x 4½
Stephen C. Clark, New York

108. THE PIPES OF PAN. 1923
Oil on canvas, 80½ x 68⅝
The artist

109. HARLEQUIN WITH GUITAR. *Dated* 1924
Oil on canvas, 51¼ x 38¼
Mr. and Mrs. Leigh B. Block, Chicago

109 a. RAM'S HEAD. Juan-les-Pins, *dated* 1925
Oil on canvas, 32⅛ x 39½
Private Collection, New York

110. THREE DANCERS. 1925
Oil on canvas, 84⅝ x 56¼
The artist

111. PAUL AS HARLEQUIN. *Dated* 1924
Oil on canvas, 51⅛ x 38⅛
The artist

112. PAUL AS PIERROT. *Dated* 28 February 1925
Oil on canvas, 51⅛ x 38⅛
The artist

113. GUITAR. 1926
String, pasted paper, oil paint, cloth and nails on
canvas, 51¼ x 38¼
The artist

114. FIGURE. 1927
Oil on wood, 51⅛ x 38⅛
The artist

115. SEATED WOMAN. *Dated* 1927
Oil on wood, 51⅛ x 38¼
Mr. and Mrs. James Thrall Soby, New Canaan,
Connecticut

116. HEAD. 1927
Oil and plaster on canvas, 39¼ x 31¾
Art Institute of Chicago, gift of Mr. and Mrs.
Samuel A. Marx

117. BATHER AND CABIN. Dinard, *dated* 1928
Oil on canvas, 8½ x 6¼
Museum of Modern Art, Hillman Periodicals
Fund

118. PAINTER AND MODEL. *Dated* 1928
Oil on canvas, 51⅝ x 63⅞
Mr. and Mrs. Sidney Janis, New York

119. RUNNING MONSTER. *Dated* April 1928
Oil on canvas, 63¾ x 51¼
The artist

120. FIGURE BY THE SEA. *Dated* 1929
Oil on canvas, 51 x 38
Florene and Samuel Marx, Chicago

121. WOMAN IN ARMCHAIR. *Dated* 5 May 1929
Oil on canvas, 76¾ x 51⅛
The artist

122. SEATED BATHER. Early 1930
Oil on canvas, 64¼ x 51
Museum of Modern Art, Mrs. Simon Guggenheim
Fund

123. CRUCIFIXION. Paris, *dated* 7 February 1930
Oil on wood, 20 x 26
The artist

124. PITCHER AND BOWL OF FRUIT. Paris,
dated 22 February 1931
Oil on canvas, 51¼ x 64
Nelson A. Rockefeller, New York

125. STILL LIFE ON TABLE. *Dated* 11 March 1931
Oil on canvas, 76¾ x 51⅝
The artist

126. DESIGN FOR SCULPTURE. 1932
Crayon on canvas, 36⅜ x 28¾
G. David Thompson, Pittsburgh

127. NUDE ON BLACK COUCH. Paris, *dated*
9 March 1932
Oil on canvas, 63¾ x 51¼
Mrs. Meric Callery, New York

128. GIRL BEFORE MIRROR. Paris, *dated*
14 March 1932
Oil on canvas, 63¾ x 51¼
Museum of Modern Art, gift of Mrs. Simon
Guggenheim

129. BATHER PLAYING BALL. Boisgeloup, *dated*
30 August 1932
Oil on canvas, 57½ x 45
The artist

130. "MINOTAURE" (design for magazine cover). 1933
Pencil drawing with pasted papers and cloth
tacked on wood, 19⅛ x 16⅛
Private collection, New York

131. THE MINOTAUR. Boisgeloup, *dated* 24 June 1933
Pen and ink wash, 18⅞ x 24¾
Sylvester W. Labrot, Jr., Hobe Sound, Florida

132. SCULPTOR AND HIS STATUE. Cannes, *dated*
20 July 1933
Gouache and ink, 15⅜ x 19⅜ (sight)
Private collection, New York

133. THE BALCONY. Cannes, *dated* 1 August 1933
Watercolor and ink, 15¾ x 19⅞
Mrs. Louise Smith, New York

134. MAN RAY. Paris, *dated* 3 January 1934
Pen and ink wash, 13⅝ x 9¾
Clifford Odets, Beverly Hills

135. STUDY FOR ILLUSTRATION TO "LYSISTRATA."
Paris, *dated* 11 January 1934
Brush and ink, 14¼ x 19⅞
Mrs. Meric Callery, New York

136. BULLFIGHT. Boisgeloup, *dated* 9 September 1934
Oil on canvas, 13 x 16⅛
Henry P. McIlhenny, Philadelphia

137. GIRL WRITING. *Dated* 1934
Oil on canvas, 63⅞ x 51⅜
Florene and Samuel Marx, Chicago

138. HARLEQUIN (project for a monument).
Paris, *dated* 10 March 1935
Oil on canvas, 24¼ x 20
Room of Contemporary Art Collection, Albright
Art Gallery, Buffalo

139. WOMAN WITH HAT. Paris, 1935
Oil on canvas, 23⅝ x 19¼
Georges A. Salles, Paris

140. RECLINING NUDE. Paris, *dated*
12 August—2 October 1936
Oil on canvas, 51¼ x 63¾
Private collection, Paris

141. PORTRAIT OF D. M. Paris, *dated*
19 November 1936
Oil on canvas, 25¼ x 20¼
Mme Marie Cuttoli, Paris

142. WOMAN SEATED BEFORE MIRROR.
Tremblay-sur-Mauldre, *dated* 16 February 1937
Oil on canvas, 51¼ x 76¾
Mr. and Mrs. Henry Clifford, Radnor, Pa.

GUERNICA — 1937

Mural No. 188   Studies Nos. 143-187

Guernica, the ancient capital of the Basque people in northern Spain, was largely destroyed on April 27, 1937, by German bombers flying for General Franco.

Some months earlier Picasso had been commissioned to paint a mural in the Spanish Republic building at the Paris World's Fair. He had done nothing about it until the news of the Guernica catastrophe aroused him to a fury of action. On May 1st he made the first sketches; on May 10th he began to paint; in June the mural was installed. There have been many and often contradictory interpretations of the *Guernica*. Picasso himself has denied it any political significance stating simply that the mural expresses his abhorrence of war and brutality.

The *Guernica* and the studies and "postscripts" listed below are lent by the artist. Only Nos. 143, 152, 156 and 188 are here illustrated; almost all are reproduced in *Guernica* by Juan Larrea, New York, Curt Valentin, 1947.

43- COMPOSITION STUDIES. *Dated* 1 May 1937
45. Pencil on blue paper, 8¼ x 10⅝ each

46- STUDIES FOR THE HORSE. *Dated* 1 May 1937
47. Pencil on blue paper, 8¼ x 10½ each

48. COMPOSITION STUDY. *Dated* 1 May 1937
Pencil on gesso on wood, 21½ x 25½

49. COMPOSITION STUDY. *Dated* 2 May 1937
Pencil on gesso on wood, 23⅝ x 28¾

150. STUDY FOR HORSE'S HEAD. *Dated* 2 May 1937
Pencil on blue paper, 8¼ x 6

151. STUDY FOR HORSE'S HEAD. *Dated* 2 May 1937
Pencil on blue paper, 10½ x 8¼

152. HORSE'S HEAD. *Dated* 2 May 1937
Oil on canvas, 25½ x 36¼

153. COMPOSITION STUDY. *Dated* 8 May 1937
Pencil on white paper, 9½ x 17⅞

154. HORSE AND WOMAN WITH DEAD CHILD.
Dated 8 May 1937
Pencil on white paper, 9½ x 17⅞

155. MOTHER WITH DEAD CHILD. *Dated* 9 May 1937
Ink on white paper, 9½ x 17⅞

156. COMPOSITION STUDY. *Dated* 9 May 1937
Pencil on white paper, 9½ x 17⅞

157. MOTHER WITH DEAD CHILD ON LADDER.
Dated 9 May 1937
Pencil on white paper, 17⅞ x 9½

158. STUDY FOR THE HORSE. *Dated* 10 May 1937
Pencil on white paper, 9½ x 17⅞

159. STUDIES FOR THE HORSE. *Dated* 10 May 1937
Pencil on white paper, 17⅞ x 9½

160. BULL'S HEAD WITH HUMAN FACE.
Dated 10 May 1937
Pencil on white paper, 17⅞ x 9½

161. STUDY FOR THE HORSE. *Dated* 10 May 1937
Pencil and color crayon on white paper,
9½ x 17⅞

162. MOTHER WITH DEAD CHILD ON LADDER.
Dated 10 May 1937
Color crayon and pencil on white paper,
17⅞ x 9½

163. BULL WITH HUMAN FACE. *Dated* 11 May 1937
Pencil on white paper, 9½ x 17⅞

164. WOMAN'S HEAD. *Dated* 13 May 1937
Pencil and color crayon on white paper,
17⅞ x 9½

165. HAND WITH BROKEN SWORD. *Dated* 13 May 1937
Pencil on white paper, 9½ x 17⅞

166. MOTHER WITH DEAD CHILD. *Dated* 13 May 1937
Color crayon and pencil on white paper,
9½ x 17⅞

167. HORSE'S HEAD. *Dated* 20 May 1937
Pencil and wash on white paper, 11½ x 9¼

168. HORSE'S HEAD. *Dated* 20 May 1937
Pencil and wash on white paper, 9¼ x 11½

169- STUDIES FOR BULL'S HEAD. *Dated* 20 May 1937
170. Pencil and wash on white paper, 9¼ x 11½ each

171. WOMAN'S HEAD. *Dated* 20 May 1937
Pencil and wash on white paper, 11½ x 9¼

172- STUDIES FOR WEEPING HEAD. *Dated* 24 May 1937
173. Pencil and wash on white paper, 11½ x 9¼ each

174. HEAD. *Dated* 24 May 1937
Pencil and wash on white paper, 9¼ x 11½

175. WEEPING HEAD. *Dated* 27 May 1937
Pencil and wash on white paper, 9¼ x 11½

176. FALLING MAN. *Dated* 27 May 1937
Pencil and wash on white paper, 9¼ x 11½

177. MOTHER WITH DEAD CHILD. *Dated* 28 May 1937
Pencil, color crayon, gouache and hair on white
paper, 9¼ x 11½

178. MOTHER WITH DEAD CHILD. *Dated* 28 May 1937
Pencil, color crayon and gouache on white paper,
9¼ x 11½

179. WEEPING HEAD. *Dated* 31 May 1937
Pencil, color crayon and gouache on white paper,
9¼ x 11½

180- STUDIES FOR WEEPING HEAD. *Dated* 3 June 1937
182. Pencil, color crayon and gouache on white paper,
9¼ x 11½ each

183. STUDY FOR MAN'S HEAD. *Dated* 4 June 1937
Pencil and wash on white paper, 9¼ x 11½

184. STUDY FOR HAND. *Dated* 4 June 1937
Pencil and wash on white paper, 9¼ x 11½

185. WEEPING HEAD. *Dated* 8 June 1937
Pencil, color crayon and wash on white paper,
11½ x 9¼

186. WEEPING HEAD. *Dated* 8 June 1937
Pencil and wash on white paper, 11½ x 9¼

187. WEEPING HEAD. *Dated* 13 June 1937
Pencil and color crayon on white paper,
11½ x 9¼

188. GUERNICA. Paris, May—early June 1937
Oil on canvas, 11 ft 5½ x 25 ft. 5¾
Extended loan by the artist to the Museum of
Modern Art, New York

189. MOTHER WITH DEAD CHILD. *Dated* 22 June 1937
Pencil, color crayon and oil on canvas,
21⅝ x 18⅛

190. WEEPING HEAD WITH HANDKERCHIEF.
Dated 6 July 1937
Ink on tan paper, 6 x 4½

191. WEEPING HEAD. *Dated* 12 October 1937
Ink and pencil on white paper, 35⅜ x 23

192. FRUIT DISH AND PITCHER. Paris, *dated*
21 January 1937
Oil on canvas, 20 x 24
J. K. Thannhauser, New York

193. WEEPING WOMAN. Paris, *dated* 26 October 1937
Oil on canvas, 24 x 19⅝
Mr. and Mrs. Roland Penrose, London

194. MAÏA WITH A SAILOR DOLL. Paris, *dated*
16 January 1938
Oil on canvas, 28¾ x 23⅝
The artist

195. GIRL WITH COCK. Paris, *dated* 15 February 1938
Oil on canvas, 57¼ x 47½
Mrs. Meric Callery, New York

196. COCK. Paris, *dated* 29 March 1938
Pastel, 30½ x 21¼
Mr. and Mrs. Ralph F. Colin, New York

197. THREE WOMEN. Mougins, *dated* 10 August 1938
Pen and ink wash, 17½ x 26⅝
Mrs. Meric Callery, New York

198. MAN WITH LOLLIPOP. Mougins, *dated*
20 August 1938
Oil on paper on canvas, 26⅞ x 18
Edward A. Bragaline, New York

199. STILL LIFE WITH BLACK BULL'S HEAD.
Paris, *dated* 19 November 1938
Oil on canvas, 38¼ x 51¼
Colonel Valdemar Ebbesen, Oslo

200. STILL LIFE WITH RED BULL'S HEAD.
Paris, *dated* 26 November 1938
Oil on canvas, 37¾ x 51
Mr. and Mrs. William A. M. Burden, New York

201. STILL LIFE. Paris, *dated* 4 February 1939
Oil on canvas, 13 x 18
Dr. Herschel Carey Walker, New York

202. PORTRAIT OF D. M. Paris, *dated* 1 April 1939
Oil on canvas, 36⅛ x 28⅝
Mlle Dora Maar, Paris

203. PORTRAIT OF D. M. Royan, *dated*
30 December 1939
Gouache, 18⅛ x 15
André Lefèvre, Paris

204. NIGHT FISHING AT ANTIBES. August 1939
Oil on canvas, 6 ft. 9 x 11 ft 4
Museum of Modern Art, Mrs. Simon Guggenheim
Fund

205. WOMAN DRESSING HER HAIR. Royan, *dated*
6 March 1940 on stretcher (but possibly early
June 1940)
Oil on canvas, 51¼ x 38⅛
The artist

206. STILL LIFE WITH SAUSAGE. Paris, *dated*
10 May 1941
Oil on canvas, 36⅛ x 25⅝
Mr. and Mrs. Victor W. Ganz, New York

207. SERENADE (L'Aubade). Paris, *dated* 4 May 1942
Oil on canvas, 6 ft. 4¾ x 8 ft. 8¼
Musée National d'Art Moderne, Paris

208. WOMAN IN GRAY. Paris, *dated* 6 August 1942
Oil on wood, 39¼ x 31⅞
Mr. and Mrs. Alex L. Hillman, New York

209. PORTRAIT OF D. M. Paris, *dated* 9 October 1942
Oil on canvas, 36¼ x 28¾
Mlle Dora Maar, Paris

210. FIRST STEPS. Paris, *dated* 21 May 1943
Oil on canvas, 51¼ x 38¼
Stephen C. Clark, New York

211. WOMAN IN GREEN. *Dated* 1943
Oil on canvas, 51 x 38
Private collection, New York

212. THE STRIPED BODICE. Paris, *dated*
20 September 1943
Oil on canvas, 40 x 32½
Nelson A. Rockefeller, New York

212 a. STILL LIFE WITH CANDLE. Paris, *dated*
4 April 1944
Oil on canvas, 23⅝ x 36¼
Jacques Sarlie, New York

213. WOMAN WASHING HER FEET. Paris, *dated*
6 May 1944
Pencil, 19⅞ x 15⅛
Art Institute of Chicago, bequest of Curt Valentin

214. WOMAN WASHING HER FEET. Paris, *dated*
10 July 1944
Brush and ink, 20 x 13¼
Museum of Modern Art

215. STILL LIFE. Paris, *dated* 20 July 1944
(presented to Matisse 1944)
Oil on canvas, 15 x 18½
Private collection

216. TOMATO PLANT. Paris, *dated* 3 August 1944
Oil on canvas, 28¾ x 36¼
Guennol Collection, New York

217. YOUNG BOY. Paris, *dated* 13-15 August 1944
Ink and wash, 19½ x 11⅛ (sight)
Florene and Samuel Marx, Chicago

218. BURNING LOGS. Paris, *dated* 4 January 1945
Pen and ink with crayon, 19½ x 23½
Mr. and Mrs. Walter Bareiss, Greenwich,
Connecticut

219. NOTRE DAME DE PARIS. *Dated* 1 March 1945
Oil on canvas, 21¼ x 32
Herbert and Nannette Rothschild, New York,
courtesy Perls Galleries

220. SEATED WOMAN. *Dated* 1946
Oil on canvas, 51 x 35
Mr. and Mrs. Victor W. Ganz, New York

221. NYMPH AND FAUNS. Antibes, 1946
Pencil and watercolor, 19¾ x 25⅞
Herbert Hemphill, Jr., New York

222. THE MIRROR. *Dated* 23 June 1947
Oil on canvas, 24 x 19⅝
Mr. and Mrs. William A. M. Burden, New York

223. CLAUDE IN POLISH COSTUME. Vallauris,
dated 23 October 1948
Oil on canvas, 47⅝ x 19⅝
The artist

224. THE KITCHEN. Vallauris, *dated* 9 November 1948
Oil on canvas, 68⅞ x 98⅜
The artist

225. PORTRAIT OF A PAINTER, AFTER EL GRECO.
Vallauris, *dated* 22 February 1950
Oil on wood, 40 x 32¼
Siegfried Rosengart, Lucerne

226. CLAUDE AND PALOMA. Vallauris, *dated*
20 January 1950
Oil on wood, 45¾ x 35
The artist

227. PALOMA PLAYING. Vallauris, *dated*
2 February 1950
Oil on wood, 49¼ x 40⅛
The artist

228. WINTER LANDSCAPE. Vallauris,
22 December 1950
Oil on wood, 40½ x 49½
Mr. and Mrs. Victor W. Ganz, New York

229. SMOKE AT VALLAURIS. *Dated* 12 January 1951
Oil on canvas, 23⅝ x 28¾
The artist

230. SPORT OF PAGES or THE KNIGHT. Vallauris,
dated 24 February 1951
Oil on canvas, 21¼ x 25½
The artist

231. THURSDAY. Vallauris, *dated* 14 June 1951
Oil on plywood, 41¼ x 53⅞
The artist

232. MME H. P. Vallauris, *dated* 30 September 1952
Oil on wood, 53½ x 41⅜
The artist

233. MME H. P. *Dated* 4 October 1952
Oil on wood, 57½ x 37¾
The artist

234. PALOMA ASLEEP. Vallauris, *dated*
28 December 1952
Oil on wood, 44⅞ x 57½
The artist

235. THE READER. Vallauris, *dated* 29 January 1953
Oil on wood, 36¼ x 28⅝
Art Institute of Chicago, gift of Mr. and Mrs.
Arnold H. Maremont through Kate Maremont
Foundation

236. CHINESE COMMODE. *Dated* 22 March 1953
Oil on wood, 57½ x 45
Saidenberg Gallery, New York

237. THE STUDIO (Painter and Model).
Dated 24 December 1953
Brush and ink, 13⅞ x 10⅜
Mr. and Mrs. Morton G. Neumann, Chicago

238. THE STUDIO (Circus). *Dated* 10 January 1954
Brush and ink, 9½ x 12⅝
Private collection, New York

239. THE STUDIO (Visit). *Dated* 17 January 1954
Brush and ink, 9½ x 12⅝
Nelson A. Rockefeller, New York

240. THE STUDIO (The Lady Painter). *Dated*
21 January 1954
Brush and ink, 9½ x 12⅝
Mr. and Mrs. Daniel Saidenberg, New York

241. THE STUDIO (Models). *Dated* 21 January 1954
Brush and ink, 9½ x 12⅝
Nelson A. Rockefeller, New York

242. THE STUDIO (King and Model). *Dated*
1 February 1954
Crayon, 9½ x 12⅝
Mr. and Mrs. Daniel Saidenberg, New York

243. PORTRAIT OF J. R. WITH ROSES. Vallauris,
dated 2 June 1954
Oil on canvas, 39⅜ x 31⅞
The artist

THE WOMEN OF ALGIERS, AFTER DELACROIX.
In Paris between December 13, 1954, and February 14, 1955, Picasso painted 15 canvases based upon Delacroix's *Les Femmes d'Alger* (1834) now in the Louvre. The whole series was brought to the United States by Mr. and Mrs. Victor W. Ganz of New York, who retain the final as well as several earlier versions. Ten are illustrated here, the final version in color. The complete series is reproduced in the catalogue of the *Picasso 1955* exhibition, Musée des Arts Décoratifs, Paris, where they were first shown. All are painted in oil on canvas and dated on the back by the artist.

244. 13 December 1954. 23⅝ x 28¾
Dr. Herschel Carey Walker, New York

245. 28 December 1954. 21¼ x 25⅝
Mr. and Mrs. Victor W. Ganz, New York

246. 16 January 1955. 18⅛ x 21⅝
Mr. and Mrs. Wilbur D. May, Reno

247. 17 January 1955. 21¼ x 25⅝
Mr. and Mrs. Daniel Saidenberg, New York

248. 18 January 1955. 25⅝ x 21¼
Saidenberg Gallery, New York

249. 24 January 1955. 51⅛ x 63¾
Mr. and Mrs. Victor W. Ganz, New York

250. 26 January 1955. 44⅞ x 57½
Paul Rosenberg and Co., New York

251. 6 February 1955. 51⅛ x 63¾
Mr. and Mrs. Victor W. Ganz, New York

252. 9 February 1955. 51⅛ x 38⅛
Paul Rosenberg and Co., New York

253. 11 February 1955. 51¼ x 76¾
Mr. and Mrs. Victor W. Ganz, New York

254. 13 February 1955. 44⅞ x 57½
Paul Rosenberg and Co., New York

255. Final version. 14 February 1955. 44⅞ x 57½
(color plate)
Mr. and Mrs. Victor W. Ganz, New York

256. THE STUDIO. *Dated* 24 October 1955
Oil on canvas, 74⅞ x 31½
Saidenberg Gallery, New York

257. SEATED WOMAN IN TURKISH COSTUME. Cannes,
dated 22 November 1955
Oil on canvas, 36¼ x 28¾
Private collection, New York

258. WOMAN IN ROCKING CHAIR. Cannes, *dated*
25 March 1956
Oil on canvas, 76⅞ x 51⅛
Galerie Louise Leiris, Paris

259. THE STUDIO. Cannes, *dated* 2 April 1956
Oil on canvas, 35 x 45⅝
Museum of Modern Art, gift of Mr. and Mrs.
Werner E. Josten

260. BULLFIGHT. Cannes, *dated* 19 May 1956
Oil on canvas, 19⅝ x 24
Mr. and Mrs. Daniel Saidenberg, New York

261. JARDINIÈRE WITH FERNS. Cannes, *dated*
5 June 1956
Oil on canvas, 63¾ x 51⅛
Mr. and Mrs. Victor W. Ganz, New York

262. WOMAN BY A WINDOW. Cannes, *dated*
11 June 1956
Oil on canvas, 63⅞ x 51¼
Lent anonymously

Illustrations
of the *Paintings* and *Drawings*

7. *Self Portrait*, 1901. Oil on canvas, 29 x 23¼. Private collection, New York

3. *Page of Studies*, 1900. Conté crayon, 5⅛ x 8¼. Ivan L. Best

1. *Redemption*, c. 1898. Watercolor and conté crayon, 17¾ x 11½. Mr. and Mrs. Justin K. Thannhauser

2. *The Artist's Sister*, 1899. Oil on canvas, 59 x 39½. The artist

5. *Self Portrait*, 1901. Oil on cardboard, 20¼ x 12½. Ambassador and Mrs. John Hay Whitney

6. *Woman's Head*, 1901. Oil on millboard, 18½ x 12. Philadelphia Museum of Art

4. *Le Moulin de la Galette*, 1900. Oil on canvas, 35¼ x 45¾. Mr. and Mrs. Justin K. Thannhauser

8. *Woman in Blue*, c. 1901. Oil on canvas, 52⅝ x 39¾. Museo Nacional de Arte Moderno, Madrid

9. *Dwarf Dancer*, 1901. Oil on canvas, 41⅝ x 23¾. Museo de Arte Moderno, Barcelona

10. *Harlequin Propped on Elbow*, 1901. Oil on canvas, 33 x 24¾. Mr. and Mrs. Henry Clifford

11. *Sebastián Junyer Vidal*, 1903. Oil on canvas, 49⅜ x 36. Sebastián Junyer Vidal

12. *Blind Man's Meal*, 1903.
Oil on canvas, 37½ x 37¼.
Metropolitan Museum of Art

13. *Brooding Woman*, 1904. Watercolor, 10⅝ x 14½.
Museum of Modern Art

14. *Woman with Chignon*, 1904.
Gouache, 16⅞ x 12¼. Art Institute of Chicago

15. *Woman with Crow*, 1904. Gouache and pastel, 25½ x 19½.
Toledo Museum of Art

16. *Meditation*, 1904. Watercolor, 13¾ x10⅛. Mrs. Louise Smith

17. *Study for "The Actor" with profiles of Fernande*, 1904-05.
Pencil, 18½ x 12⅜. Nelson A. Rockefeller

19. *Boy on a Horse*, 1905. Charcoal, 18⅜ x 12.
Mr. and Mrs. John W. Warrington

20. *Boy with Bouquet*, 1905. Gouache, 25½ x 21⅜.
Mrs. John Wintersteen

21. *Page of Studies*, 1905. Pen and ink, 12¾ x 9¾.
Nelson A. Rockefeller

22. *Man's Head*, 1905. Watercolor, 16 x 13¾.
Mr. and Mrs. Rodolphe M. de Schauensee

23. *Boy Leading a Horse*, 1905. Oil on canvas, 87 x 51¼. Mr. and Mrs. William S. Paley

24. *Circus Family*, 1905. Watercolor and pen, 9½ x 12.
Baltimore Museum of Art

25. *Monkey*, 1905.
Watercolor and pen, 19¾ x 12⅝.
Baltimore Museum of Art

26. *Woman with Loaves*, 1906. Oil on canvas, 39
Philadelphia Museum of Art

Leo Stein, 1906. Gouache, 9¾ x 6¾.
Baltimore Museum of Art

28. *Two Nudes*, 1906. Oil on canvas, 59¾ x 36⅝. G. David Thompson

29. *Peasants from Andorra*, 1906. Ink, 27⅞ x 16½. Art Institute of Chicago

30. *Two Women*, 1906. Charcoal, 24¾ x 18½.
Mr. and Mrs. Richard S. Davis

32. *Woman Combing Her Hair*, 1906. Oil on canvas, 49¾ x 35½.
Florene and Samuel Marx

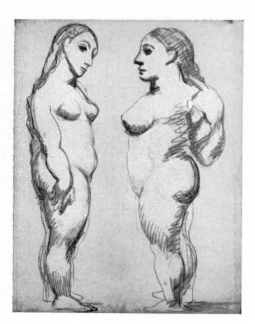

31. *Two Nudes*, 1906. Pencil and estompe, 24¾ x 18½.
Art Institute of Chicago

. *Landscape*, 1906. Oil on canvas, 27½ x 39. Mr. and Mrs. Nate B. Spingold

4. *The Blind Flower Vendor*, 1906. Ink and atercolor, 25 x 18¾. Mr. and Mrs. S. J. Zacks

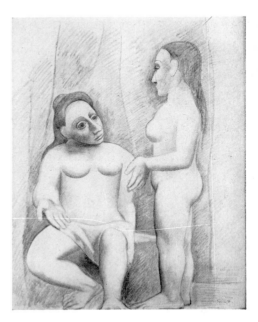

35. *Woman Seated and Woman Standing*, 1906. Charcoal, 24⅛ x 18¼. Philadelphia Museum of Art

36. *Gertrude Stein*, 1906. Oil on canvas, 39⅜ x 32.
Metropolitan Museum of Art

37. *Study for "Les Demoiselles d'Avignon,"* 1907.
Charcoal and pastel, 18⅞ x 25. The artist

38. *Study for "Les Demoiselles d'Avignon,"* 1907.
Watercolor, 6¾ x 8¾. Philadelphia Museum of Art

Les Demoiselles d'Avignon, 1907. Oil on canvas, 96 x 92. Museum of Modern Art

40. *Harvesters*, 1907.
Oil on canvas, 25⅝ x 31⅞.
Nelson A. Rockefeller

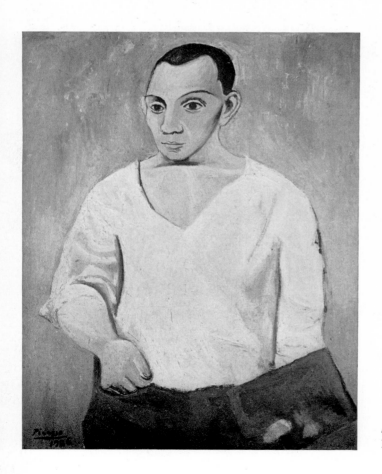

41. *Self Portrait*, 1906. Oil on canvas. 36½ x 28¾
Philadelphia Museum of Art

42. *Flowers*, 1907. Oil on canvas, 36½ x 28½.
Mr. and Mrs. Ralph F. Colin

Jug and Bowl, 1907. Oil on wood, 24½ x 19.
ivate collection

43a. *Grand Dancer of Avignon*, 1907.
Oil on canvas, 59 x 39½.
Walter P. Chrysler, Jr.

44. *Bathers in the Forest*, 1908. Watercolor, 19⅛ x 23¾.
Mrs. Eleanor Rixson Cannon

45. *Woman Sleeping*, 1908. Oil on canvas, 32 x 25½.
André Lefèvre

Seated Woman, 1908. Oil on canvas, 28¾ x 23½.
ry Aldrich

47. *Kneeling Figure*, 1908. Charcoal, 24⅜ x 18½.
Nelson A. Rockefeller

48. *Woman's Head*, 1909. Black crayon and
gouache, 24¼ x 18¾. Art Institute of Chicago

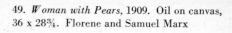

49. *Woman with Pears*, 1909. Oil on canvas,
36 x 28¾. Florene and Samuel Marx

51. *Nude*, 1910. Charcoal, 19⅛ x 12¼
Metropolitan Museum of Art

50. *Female Nude*, 1910. Pen and ink and watercolor, 29⅛ x 18⅜.
Mr. and Mrs. Richard S. Davis

52. *Girl with Mandolin,* 1910. Oil on canvas, 39½ x 29.
Nelson A. Rockefeller

Wilhelm Uhde, 1910. Oil on canvas, 32 x 23¾.
and Mrs. Roland Penrose

54. *D. H. Kahnweiler,* 1910. Oil on canvas, 39⅝ x 28⅝.
Art Institute of Chicago

56. *"Le Torero,"* 1911. Oil on canvas, 18¼ x 15.
Nelson A. Rockefeller

57. *Man with Pipe,* 1911. Ink wash with
charcoal, probably oil, 25 x 18¼.
Fogg Art Museum

55. *Female Nude,* 1910. Oil on canvas, 38¾ x 30⅜.
Philadelphia Museum of Art

57a. *L'Independant*, 1911. Oil on canvas, 24 x 19¾.
Mr. and Mrs. Henry Clifford

, *"Ma Jolie,"* 1911-12. Oil on canvas, 39⅜ x 25¾.
useum of Modern Art

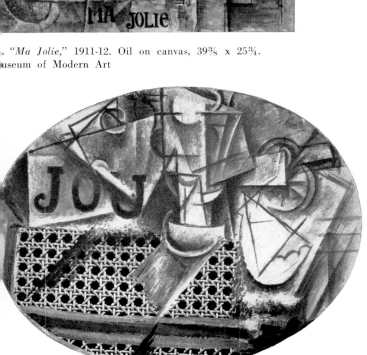

60. *Still Life with Chair Caning*, 1911-12. Oil, pasted oilcloth
simulating chair caning on canvas, 10⅝ x 13¾. The artist

59. *Bottle of "Vieux Marc," Glass,
Newspaper*, 1912. Charcoal and pasted papers,
24⅝ x 18½. Mme Marie Cuttoli

61. *Aficionado*, 1912. Oil on canvas, 53¼ x 32½.
Oeffentliche Kunstsammlung, Kunstmuseum, Basle

62. *Man with Pipe*, 1912. Charcoal, 24½ x 18½. Dr. and Mrs. Israel Rosen

65. *Man's Head*, 1912-13.
Charcoal, 24½ x 18⅝. Private collection

un with Guitar, 1912. Oil on canvas, 51⅞ x 35.
lelphia Museum of Art

64. *Guitar*, 1912. Oil on canvas, 28½ x 23⅝.
Nasjonalgalleriet, Oslo

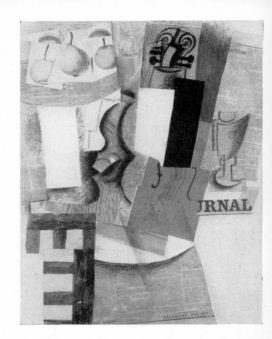

68. *Violin and Fruit*, 1913. Charcoal and pasted papers, 25½ x 19½. Philadelphia Museum of Art

66. *Man with Violin*, 1912-13. Charcoal and pasted papers, 48⅝ x 18⅛.
G. David Thompson

67. *Still Life (Bottle and Glass)*, 1912-13. Charcoal, ink and pasted paper, 24⅞ x 19⅛. Metropolitan Museum of Art

69. *Violin and Guitar*, 1913. Pasted cloth, oil, pencil and plaster on canvas, 36 x 25. Philadelphia Museum of Art

71. *Bird*, 1913.
Oil on canvas, 13 x 5⅞.
Private collection

70. *Guitar*, 1913. Charcoal and pasted papers, 24½ x 18½. Nelson A. Rockefeller

71a. *Woman in an Armchair*, 1913. Oil on canvas, 59¼ x 39⅜. Mrs. Ingeborg Pudelko Eichmann

72. *Card Player*, 1913-14. Oil on canvas, 42½ x 35¼. Museum of Modern Art

73. *Head, c.* 1914. Charcoal and pasted papers
on cardboard, 17⅛ x 13⅛.
Mr. and Mrs. Roland Penrose

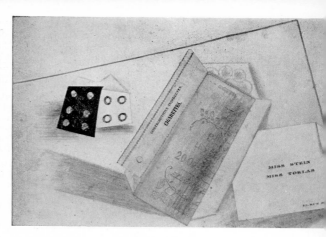

74. *Still Life with Calling Card,* 1914. Pencil and pasted pa
5½ x 8¼. Mrs. Gilbert W. Chapman

75. *Pipe, Glass, Bottle of Rum,* 1914. Pencil, gouache
and pasted papers on cardboard, 15¾ x 20¾.
Museum of Modern Art

76. *Ambroise Vollard,* 1915. Pencil, 18⅜ x 12½.
Metropolitan Museum of Art

77. *Harlequin*, 1915. Oil on canvas, 72¼ x 41⅜. Museum of Modern Art

79. *Man with Pipe*, c. 1915. Oil on canvas, 51¼ x 35¼. Art Institute of Chicago

78. *Head of a Young Man*, 1915.
Oil on wood, 10 x 7¼.
Mrs. Louise Smith

80. *Bathers*, 1918. Pencil, 9⅛ x 12¼. Fogg Art Museum

81. *Pierrot and Harlequin*, 1918.
Pencil, 10¼ x 7½. Art Institute of Chicago

82. *Fisherman*, 1918. Pencil, 13¾ x 10.
Private collection

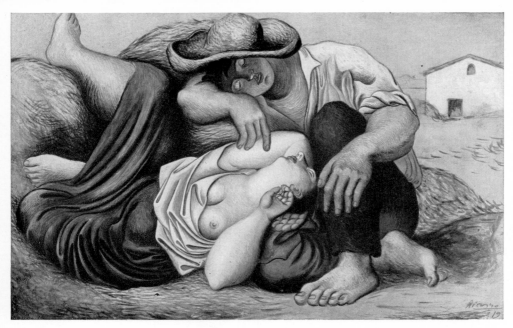

83. *Sleeping Peasants*, 1919. Gouache, 12¼ x 19¼. Museum of Modern Art

84. *Three Ballerinas*, 1919.
Pencil and charcoal, 23⅛ x 17⅜. The artist

85. *Diaghilev and Selisburg*, 1919.
Pencil, 24⅞ x 18⅞. The artist

Peasant Bride and Groom, 1919. Conté
on, 23½ x 18¼. Santa Barbara Museum of Art

87. *Two Ballet Dancers,* 1919.
Pencil, 12¼ x 9¼.
Mr. and Mrs. Victor W. Ganz

Page of Sketches, 1919.
il, 12½ x 8⅝. Mrs. Culver Orswell

89. *Landscape,* 1920. Oil on canvas, 20½ x 27½. The artist

90. *By the Sea*, 1920. Oil on wood, 32 x 39½. G. David Thompson.

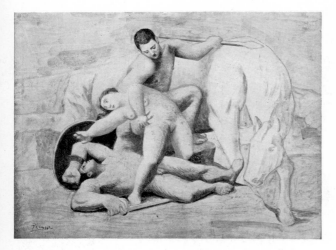

91. *The Rape*, 1920. Tempera on wood, 9⅜ x 12⅞.
Philip L. Goodwin

92. *Pierrot and Harlequin*, 1920.
Gouache, 10⅛ x 7¾.
Mrs. Gilbert W. Chapman

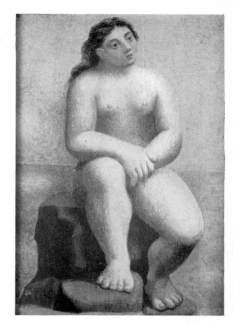

96. *Nude Seated on a Rock*, 1921.
Tempera on wood, 6¼ x 4¾.
Mr. and Mrs. James Thrall Soby

Nessus and Dejanira Studies, 1920.

93. Pencil, 8¼ x 10¼.
Museum of Modern Art

94. Watercolor, 8½ x 11¼.
Private collection

95. Silverpoint, 8⅜ x 10⅝.
Nelson A. Rockefeller

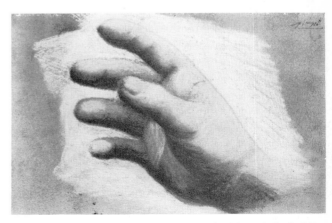

97. *Study of a Hand*, 1921. Pastel, 8⅛ x 12½. Nelson A. Rockefeller

98. *Three Musicians*, 1921. Oil on canvas, 80 x 74. Philadelphia Museum of Art

99. *Three Musicians*, 1921. Oil on canvas, 79 x 87¾. Museum of Modern Art

99a. *Three Women at the Spring*, 1921.
Oil on canvas, 80¼ x 68½.
Museum of Modern Art

100. *Mother and Child*, 1921.
Oil on canvas, 56½ x 64.
Art Institute of Chicago

The Race, 1922. Tempera on wood, 12⅞ x 16¼. The artist

102. *Standing Nude*, 1922. Oil on wood, 7½ x 5½.
Wadsworth Atheneum

103. *Mandolin on a Table*, 1922. Oil on canvas, 32½ x 39⅜. Mr. and Mrs. William B. Jaffe

104. *Dr. Claribel Cone,* 1922. Pencil, 24¾ x 19¼.
Baltimore Museum of Art

105. *St. Servan, near Dinard,* 1922. Pencil, 16⅛ x 1
Mr. and Mrs. Justin K. Thannhauser

106. *Standing Nude,* 1922. Oil on canvas, 10¼ x 8½.
Private collection

107. *Actor in Green,* 1922. Gouache on
paper, 6⅜ x 4½. Stephen C. Clark

The Pipes of Pan, 1923. Oil on canvas, 80½ x 68⅝. The artist

109. *Harlequin with Guitar*, 1924. Oil on canvas, 51¼ x 38¼.
Mr. and Mrs. Leigh B. Block

109a. *Ram's Head*, 1925.
Oil on canvas, 32⅛ x 39½.
Private collection

110. *Three Dancers*, 1925. Oil on canvas, 84⅝ x 56¼. The artist

112. *Paul as Pierrot*, 1925. Oil on canvas, 51⅛ x 38⅛. The artist

111. *Paul as Harlequin*, 1924. Oil on canvas, 51⅛ x 38⅛. The artist

115. *Seated Woman*, 1927. Oil on wood, 51⅛ x 38¼.
Mr. and Mrs. James Thrall Soby

114. *Figure*, 1927. Oil on wood, 51⅛ x 38⅜. The artist

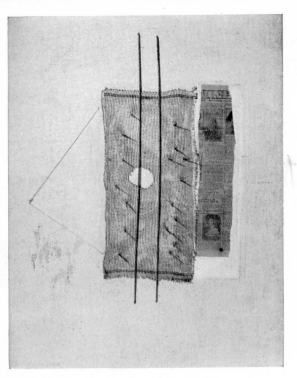

113. *Guitar*, 1926. String, pasted paper, oil paint, cloth, and nails on canvas, 51¼ x 38¼. The artist

116. *Head*, 1927. Oil and plaster on canvas, 39¼ x 31¾. Art Institute of Chicago

117. *Bather and Cabin*, 1928. Oil on canvas, 8½ x 6¼. Museum of Modern Art

118. *Painter and Model*, 1928. Oil on canvas, 51⅝ x 63⅞. Mr. and Mrs. Sidney Janis

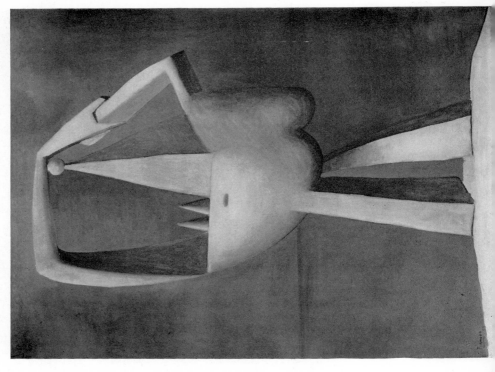

120. *Figure by the Sea*, 1929. Oil on canvas, 51 x 38. Florene and Samuel Marx

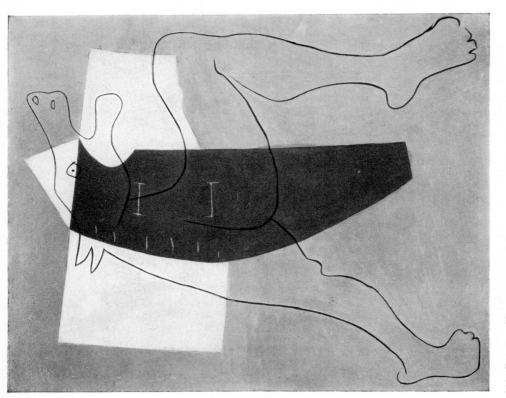

119. *Running Monster*, 1928. Oil on canvas, 63¾ x 51¼. The artist

122. *Seated Bather*, 1930. Oil on canvas, 64¼ x 51. Museum of Modern Art

121. *Woman in an Armchair*, 1929. Oil on canvas, 76¾ x 51⅛. The artist

123. *Crucifixion*, 1930. Oil on wood, 20 x 26. The artist

124. *Pitcher and Bowl of Fruit*, 1931. Oil on canvas, 51¼ x 64. Nelson A. Rockefeller

125. *Still Life on a Table*, 1931.
Oil on canvas, 76¾ x 51⅝. The artist

126. *Design for sculpture*, 1932. Crayon on canvas, 36⅜ x 28¾.
G. David Thompson

127. *Nude on a Black Couch*, 1932. Oil on canvas, 63¾ x 51¼. Mrs. Meric Callery

137. *Girl Writing*, 1934. Oil on canvas, 63⅞ x 51⅜. Florene and Samuel Marx

128. *Girl before a Mirror*, 1932. Oil on canvas, 63¾ x 51¼. Museum of Modern Art

129. *Bather Playing Ball*, 1932. Oil on canvas, 57½ x 45. The artist

31. *The Minotaur*, 1933. Pen and ink wash, 18⅞ x 24¾.
ylvester W. Labrot, Jr.

132. *Sculptor and his Statue*, 1933.
Gouache and ink, 15⅜ x 19⅜.
Private collection

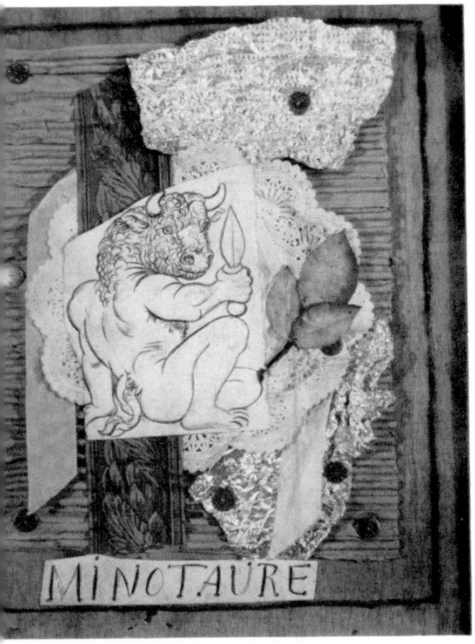

'Minotaure,'' 1933. Pencil drawing,
papers and cloth tacked on wood,
x 16⅛. Private collection

133. *The Balcony*, 1933. Watercolor and ink, 15¾ x 19⅞.
Mrs. Louise Smith

136. *Bullfight*, 1934. Oil on canvas, 13 x 16⅛.
Henry P. McIlhenny

134. *Man Ray*, 1934.
Pen and ink wash, 13⅝ x 9¾.
Clifford Odets

135. *Study for illustrations to "Lysistrata,"* 1934. Brush and ink, 14¼ x 19⅞. Mrs. Meric Callery

200. *Still Life with Red Bull's Head*, 1938. Oil on canvas, 37¾ x 51. Mr. and Mrs. William A. M. Burden

203. *Portrait of D.M.*, 1939. Gouache, 18⅛ x 15.
André Lefèvre

?2. *Portrait of D.M.*, 1939. Oil on canvas, 36⅛ x 28⅝.
Ille Dora Maar

204. *Night Fishing at Antibes*, 1939. Oil on canvas, 6 ft. 9 x 11 ft. 4. Museum of Modern Art

205. *Woman Dressing her Hair*, 1940. Oil on canvas, 51¼ x 38⅛. The artist

206. *Still Life with Sausage*, 1941. Oil on canvas, 36⅛ x 25⅝. Mr. and Mrs. Victor W. Ganz

207. *Serenade (L'Aubade)*, 1942. Oil on canvas, 6 ft. 4¾ x 8 ft. 8¼. Musée National d'Art Moderne, Paris

209. *Portrait of D.M.*, 1942. Oil on canvas, 36¼ x 28¾.
Mlle Dora Maar

208. *Woman in Gray*, 1942. Oil on wood, 39¼ x 31⅞.
Mr. and Mrs. Alex L. Hillman

210. *First Steps*, 1943.
Oil on canvas, 51¼ x 38¼.
Stephen C. Clark

212. *The Striped Bodice*, 1943. Oil on canvas, 40 x 32½
Nelson A. Rockefeller

211. *Woman in Green*, 1943. Oil on canvas, 51 x 38. Private collection

212a. *Still Life with Candle*, 1944. Oil on canvas, 23⅝ x 36¼. Jacques Sarlie

213. *Woman Washing her Feet*, 1944.
Pencil, 19⅞ x 15⅛. Art Institute of Chicago

214. *Woman Washing her Feet*, 1944. Brush
and ink, 20 x 13¼. Museum of Modern Art

216. *Tomato Plant*, 1944. Oil on canvas, 28¾ x 36¼. Guennol Collection

217. *Young Boy*, 1944. Ink and wash, 19½ x 11⅛. Florene and Samuel Marx

Still Life, 1944. Oil on canvas, 15 x 18½. Private collection.

219. *Notre Dame de Paris*, 1945. Oil on canvas, 21¼ x 32. Herbert and Nannette Rothschild

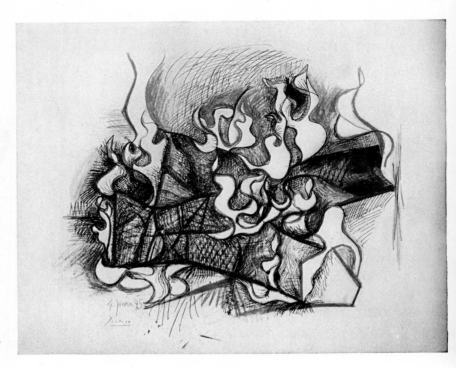

218. *Burning Logs*, 1945. Pen and ink with crayon, 19½ x 23½. Mr. and Mrs. Walter Bareiss

220. *Seated Woman*, 1946. Oil on canvas, 51 x 35.
Mr. and Mrs. Victor W. Ganz

Nymph and Fauns, 1946. Pencil and watercolor, 19¾ x 25⅞.
ert Hemphill, Jr.

222. *The Mirror*, 1947. Oil on canvas, 24 x 19⅝.
Mr. and Mrs. William A. M. Burden

223. *Claude in Polish Costume*, 1948. Oil on canvas, 47⅝ x 19⅝. The artist

224. *The Kitchen*, 1948. Oil on canvas, 68⅞ x 98⅜. The artist

225. *Portrait of a Painter, after El Greco*, 1950.
Oil on wood, 40 x 32¼. Siegfried Rosengart

227. *Paloma Playing*, 1950. Oil on wood, 49¾ x 40⅛. The artist

226. *Claude and Paloma*, 1950. Oil on wood, 45¾ x 35. The artist

228. *Winter Landscape*, 1950. Oil on wood, 40½ x 49½. Mr. and Mrs. Victor W. Ganz

230. *Sport of Pages*, 1951.
Oil on canvas, 21¼ x 25½.
The artist

229. *Smoke at Vallauris*,
1951. Oil on canvas,
23⅝ x 28¾. The artist

231. *Thursday*, 1951. Oil on
plywood, 41¼ x 53⅞. The artist

234. *Paloma Asleep*, 1952.
Oil on wood, 44⅞ x 57½.
The artist

233. *Mme H. P.*, 1952. Oil on wood, 57½ x 37¾. The artist

232. *Mme H. P.*, 1952. Oil on wood, 53½ x 41⅜. The artist

235. *The Reader*, 1953. Oil on wood, 36¼ x 28⅝. Art Institute of Chicago

236. *Chinese Commode*, 1953. Oil on wood, 57½ x 45. Saidenberg Gallery

237. *The Studio (Painter and Model)*, 1953. Brush and ink, 13⅞ x 10⅜.
Mr. and Mrs. Morton G. Neumann

238. *The Studio (Circus)*, 1954.
Brush and ink, 9½ x 12⅝. Private collecti

239. *The Studio (Visit)*, 1954. Brush and ink, 9½ x 12⅝.
Nelson A. Rockefeller

240. *The Studio (The Lady Painter)*, 1954. Brush and ink, 9½ x 12⅝. Mr. and Mrs. Daniel Saidenberg

241. *The Studio (Models)*, 1954. Brush and ink, 9½ x 12⅝. Nelson A. Rockefeller

242. *The Studio (King and Model)*, 1954. Crayon, 9½ x 12⅝. Mr. and Mrs. Daniel Saidenberg

246. 16 January 1955. 18⅛ x 21⅝.
Mr. and Mrs. Wilbur D. May

245. 28 December 1954. 21¼ x 25⅝.
Mr. and Mrs. Victor W. Ganz

244. 13 December 1954. 23⅝ x 28¾.
Dr. Herschel Carey Walker

248. 18 January 1955. 25⅝ x 21¼.
Saidenberg Gallery

249. 24 January 1955. 51⅛ x 63¾.
Mr. and Mrs. Victor W. Ganz

Women of Algiers. Final version, 14 February 1955. 44⅞ x 57½". Collection Mr. and Mrs. Victor W. Ganz, New York

254. 13 February 1955. 44⅞ x 57½. Paul Rosenberg and Co.

251. 6 February 1955. 51⅛ x 63¾. Mr. and Mrs. Victor W. Ganz

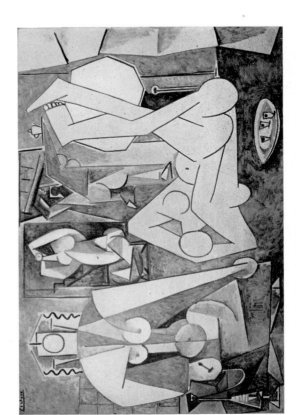

253. 11 February 1955. 51¼ x 76¾. Mr. and Mrs. Victor W. Ganz

243. *Portrait of J. R. with Roses*, 1954.
Oil on canvas, 39⅜ x 31⅞. The artist

256. *The Studio*, 1955. Oil on canvas, 74⅞ x 31½.
Saidenberg Gallery

257. *Seated Woman in Turkish Costume*, 1955.
Oil on canvas, 36¼ x 28¾. Private collection

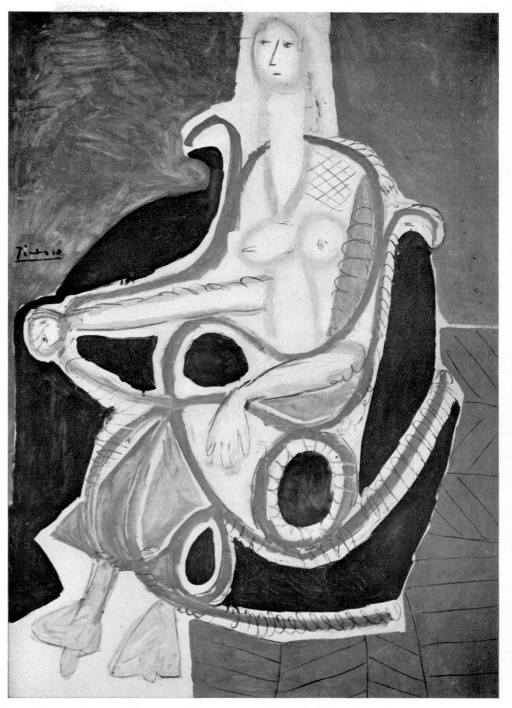

258. *Woman in Rocking Chair*, 1956. Oil on canvas, 76⅞ x 51⅛. Galerie Louise Leiris

259. *The Studio*, 1956. Oil on canvas, 35 x 45⅝. Museum of Modern Art

260. *Bullfight*, 1956. Oil on canvas, 19⅝ x 24. Mr. and Mrs. Daniel Saidenberg

262. *Woman by a Window*, 1956. Oil on canvas, 63⅞ x 51¼. Lent anonymously

261. *Jardinière with Ferns*, 1956. Oil on canvas, 63¾ x 51⅛.
Mr. and Mrs. Victor W. Ganz

Catalogue
of the
Sculpture

. SEATED WOMAN. 1899
Bronze. H. 5½
Mrs. List-Israel, New York

. MAN'S MASK. *Dated* 1904-05
Bronze. H. 7¾
Baltimore Museum of Art, Cone Collection

. FERNANDE. *Dated* 1905
Bronze. H. 14¼
Allen Memorial Art Museum, Oberlin College

. JESTER'S HEAD. Paris, 1905
Bronze. H. 15
Philadelphia Museum of Art

5. MAN'S HEAD. c. 1905
Bronze. H. 6½
J. K. Thannhauser, New York

6. WOMAN'S HEAD. 1906
Bronze. H. 6¼
Miss Clara Hoover, New York

7. KNEELING WOMAN COMBING HER HAIR. 1906
Bronze. H. 16⅝
Nelson A. Rockefeller, New York

8. GIRL'S HEAD. 1906
Bronze. H. 5⅜
Mr. and Mrs. William Zeckendorf, Jr., New York

9. WOMAN'S HEAD. 1909
Bronze. H. 16¼
Museum of Modern Art

10. GLASS OF ABSINTHE. 1914
Painted bronze, and silver spoon. H. 7⅞
Philadelphia Museum of Art

11. STILL LIFE. 1914
Painted wood with upholstery fringe. L. 18⅞
Mr. and Mrs. Roland Penrose, London

12. BY THE SEA. Juan-les-Pins, *dated* 22 August 1930
Sand over cardboard, plaster and canvas.
10⅝ x 13¾
The artist

13. STANDING WOMAN. 1931
Bronze after carved wood. H. 21½
Mrs. Meric Callery, New York

14. COCK. 1932
Bronze. H. 25½
Mr. and Mrs. William A. M. Burden, New York
(Reproduced p. 10)

7. *Kneeling Woman Combing Her Hair.* 1

3. *Fernande.* 1905

13 *Standing Woman.*

9. *Woman's Head.* 1909

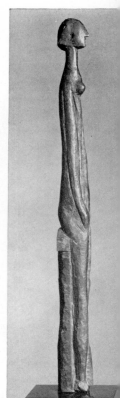

10. *Glass of Absinthe.* 1914

37. *Baboon and Young.* 1951

Man with a Lamb. Paris, 1944

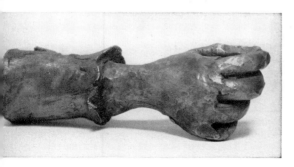

Hand. 1947

38. *Woman's Head.* 1951

15. MAN WITH A LAMB. Paris, *dated* 1944
Bronze. H. 7 ft. 4
Mr. and Mrs. R. Sturgis Ingersoll

16- GROUP OF FEMALE FIGURES. 1945-1947
32. Bronze. H. 3⅜ to 10⅛
G. David Thompson, Pittsburgh

33. HAND. 1947
Bronze. L. 9½
Mrs. H. Gates Lloyd, Haverford, Pennsylvania

34. PREGNANT WOMAN. 1950
Bronze. H. 41¼
Museum of Modern Art, gift of Mrs. Louise Smith

35. ANGRY OWL. 1950
Bronze. H. 12⅞
Mr. and Mrs. Morton G. Neumann, Chicago

36. OWL. 1950
Bronze. H. 14½
Louis E. Stern, New York

37. BABOON AND YOUNG. *Dated* 1951
Bronze. H. 21
Museum of Modern Art
Mrs. Simon Guggenheim Fund

38. WOMAN'S HEAD. 1951
Bronze. H. 21⅛
Museum of Modern Art
Benjamin and David Scharps Fund

39. GOAT SKULL AND BOTTLE. 1951-52
Painted bronze. H. 31
Museum of Modern Art
Mrs. Simon Guggenheim Fund

40. CRANE. 1952
Painted bronze. H. 29¼
G. David Thompson, Pittsburgh

41. GIRL READING A BOOK. 1952-53
Painted bronze. L. 14
Mr. and Mrs. Gerald Gidwitz,
Highland Park, Illinois

42. PITCHER AND FIGS. 1952
Painted bronze. H. 10
Mr. and Mrs. Morton G. Neumann, Chicago

43. LITTLE OWL. 1953
Painted bronze. H. 10¼
Joseph H. Hirshhorn, New York

44. LITTLE OWL. 1953
Painted bronze. H. 13
Mr. and Mrs. Victor W. Ganz, New York

45. BOUQUET. 1953
Bronze. H. 24
Galerie Louise Leiris, Paris

46. FLOWERS IN A VASE. 1953
Bronze. H. 29
Mr. and Mrs. Harry Lynde Bradley, Milwau

Catalogue of the Ceramics

NOTE: All ceramics listed below have been baked under the supervision of M. and Mme Georges Ramie at the Poterie Madoura, Vallauris. Each is an original work by Picasso, but they fall in two categories: pieces decorated and glazed by Picasso, with painted or incised designs or relief additions (Nos. 1-50). These are unique pieces. Picasso does not usually fashion the earthenware object which he decorates but suggests to M. and Mme Ramie that they make certain shapes to suit his purpose. Sometimes Picasso actually does his own modelling (*Pigeons* Nos. 12, 14 and 24). Others are stamped *'Empreinte Originale Picasso'* (Nos. 51-65, 68-72). These are produced from moulds especially prepared and carved by Picasso. There is a small edition of each, varying according to circumstances from about 10 to about 75. These are 'impressions' from Picasso's original design and may be compared to a signed and numbered edition of an original engraving or lithograph.

Another group bears the stamp *'Edition Picasso'* (Nos. 66, 67). These are copies after or interpretations of an original by Picasso, all decoration and glazing by the staff of the Poterie Madoura. Such 'editions' are unlimited. Sometimes Picasso has taken an earthenware plate or jug already stamped *'Edition Picasso'* and used it for a unique piece. This is rare but occurs in one or two works here exhibited.

Nos. 1-50 are lent by the artist.

1. GOAT AND FLUTE PLAYER. *Dated* 14 June 1948
   Plaque. 10⅝ x 8⅛. Red clay, with colored slips, incised (reproduced above)

2. STILL LIFE WITH COFFEEPOT. *Dated* August 1948
   Plaque. 39⅜ x 39⅜. Fire clay with slip and glaze decoration (reproduced p. 3)

3. FAUN FACE. *Dated* 1 February 1949
   Shallow dish. D. 14⅝. Slip underglaze with carved and relief effects; eyes and nose formed by a kilnspur

4. FISH. *Dated* 1 July 1950
   Bowl. D. 11. Incised design on red clay, heightened with white slip

5. DECORATED CRUET. c. 1951
   Six-handled vase. H. 16½. Black and blue slip on biscuit

6. FROG. c. 1951
   Six-handled vase. H. 16½. Black and blue slip on biscuit

7. MOUNTED CAVALIER. c. 1951
   Two-handled pitcher. H. 16½. Red and black oxides on white tin glaze

8. DOTS AND DABS. c. 1952
   Two-handled pot with cover. H. 16½. White tin glaze with metal oxides

9. BULLS AND FOLIAGE. c. 1952
   Two-handled vase. H. 28¾. Glazed with resist design

10. DOUBLE FACE. c. 1952
    Vase in shape of a cock. H. 26. Black slip on white fire clay

11. TWO FACES. *Dated* 6 January 1953
    Pitcher. H. 16½. Decorated with metal oxide glazes and paraffin resist

12. PIGEON STANDING. *Dated* 7 January 1953
    H. 5⅞. Black slip

13. FOUR FACES. *Dated* 26 January 1953
Vase. H. 22. Metal oxides on white tin glaze, incised

14. PIGEON ON ITS NEST. *Dated* 29 January 1953
H. 6¼. Black and blue slip

15. DABS. *Dated* 4 March 1953
Dish. D. 15¾. Black resist design

16. DABS. *Dated* 4 March 1953
Dish. D. 17⅞. Black resist design

17. FLOWERS IN A VASE. *Dated* 18 April 1953
Jug, rim rolled inward. H. 11¾. Colored slips on biscuit

18. DAISIES IN A VASE. *Dated* 18 April 1953
Jug, rim rolled inward. H. 11¾. Colored slips on biscuit painted, carved

19. SUNS AND RAYS. *Dated* 4 June 1953
Jug. H 13¾. Fire clay with pastel slips

20. FOUR FACES. *Dated* 4 June 1953
Two-handled vase. H. 13. Fire clay, pastel slips

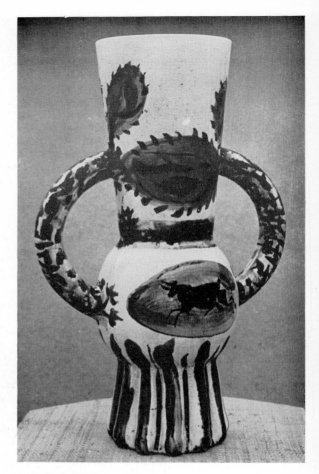

9. *Bulls and Foliage.*

10. *Double Face.*

21. WOMEN AND SILENUS HEAD. *Dated* 3 July 1953
Long-necked pitcher. H. 14⅝. Fire clay with white and black slip

22. WOMAN WITH MIRROR, GROUPS OF FIGURES. *Dated* 4 July 1953
Jug. H. 13⅜. Fire clay, white and black slip

23. BULLS. *Dated* 3 August 1953
Jug. H. 14⅝. Black slip and white glaze, incised

24. PIGEON. *Dated* 14 October 1953
H. 5½. Black slip, incised

25. LANDSCAPE. *Dated* 9 December 1953
Dish. D. 16⅞. Black slip, with incised decoration picked out with tinted glazes

26. HEAD AND GEOMETRIC MOTIFS. *Dated* 19 December 1953
Vase. H. 10½. Incised decoration, slip and glaze on red

7. Mounted Cavalier.

30. *Painter and Model.* 31. *Painter with Model.*

32. *Men's Faces.*

33. *Painter and Sculptor with Model.*   34. *Circus Act.*

LANDSCAPE. *Dated* December 1953
Dish. D. 16⅞. Glaze and white enamel on incised black slip

FIGURES. Late 1953
Jug. H. 11. White tin glaze on red, resist design

TWO HANDS HOLDING A BIRD. c. 1953
Duck-shaped pitcher. H. 15. Metal oxides on white tin glaze, incised

PAINTER AND MODEL. *Dated* 5 January 1954
Jug. H. 15. White tin glaze with resist design

PAINTER WITH MODEL. *Dated* 6 January 1954
Jug. H. 13¾. White tin glaze with resist design

MEN'S FACES. *Dated* 6 January 1954
Two-handled vase. H. 7⅞. White tin glaze with resist design

PAINTER AND SCULPTOR WITH MODEL.
Dated 7 January 1954
Jug. H. 11. White and green glazes, resist design

CIRCUS ACT. *Dated* 9 January 1954
Jug. H. 14⅛. White tin glaze with resist design

35. FACE WITH BROKEN NOSE. *Dated* 9 January 1954
Vase. H. 26¾. Incised and glazed decoration on dark ground

36. STYLIZED BIRD. *Dated* 11 January 1954
Pitcher in shape of pigeon with flat tail. H. 14⅝. Incised decoration, black slip and white glaze with touches of copper green

37. VASE OF FLOWERS. *Dated* 12 January 1954
Jug. H. 11¾. Incised and glazed decoration on black ground

38. THREE FACES. *Dated* 19 January 1954
Jug. H. 7⅛. Incised and glazed decoration on dark ground

39. MAN'S FACE. *Dated* 6 April 1954
Dish. 15¾ x 13. Carved under white glaze

40. WOMAN'S FACE. *Dated* 6 April 1954
Dish. 15¾ x 13. Carved decoration under white glaze

41. TWO BIRDS IN A CAGE. *Dated* 10 April 1954
Jug, rim rolled inward. H. 11¾. Biscuit with colored slips, carved

29. *Two Hands Holding a Bird.*

18. *Daisies in a Vase.*

42. TWO FACES. 1954
    Two-handled vase. H. 6¾. Green-black copper glaze with slip decoration

43. FACE. c. 1954
    Plate. D. 9⅞. Slip wash with glaze-filled incised design and touches of glaze.

44. FACE. c. 1954
    Plate. D. 9⅞. Colored glazes on biscuit

45. FACE. c. 1954
    Plate. D. 9⅞. Colored glazes on biscuit

46. FACE. c. 1954
    Plate. D. 9⅞. Biscuit, glaze-filled incised des

47. FACE. c. 1954
    Plate. D. 9⅞. Biscuit, black slip, colored gl

48. STYLIZED FACE. c. 1955
    Bowl. D. 8⅝. Enamelled decoration on glaze ground

49. THREE FACES AND SERPENTINES. 1956
    Long-necked pitcher. H. 15¾. Carved bis

50. GIRL IN CHARIOT DRAWN BY FAUN
    Plaque. 9⅞ x 13. Metal oxides on white glaze

Nos. 51-72 are lent by the Poterie Madoura, Vallau
All are produced from moulds and are in w
biscuit except where noted.

51. WOMAN'S FACE. *Dated* 20 March 1954
    Jug. H. 9

52. JACQUELINE ROQUE. *Dated* 29 January 1955
    Plate. D. 16½

64. *Large Vase with Fish.*

a-f are in red clay; each piece D. 6¾

a. HEAD OF SYLVETTE. *Dated* 31 March 1955

b. FISH. *Dated* 31 March 1955

c. FISHERMAN UNDER A TREE. Dated 6 March 1955

d. HEAD OF A FAUN. *Dated* 30 March 1955

e. GRASSHOPPER. *Dated* 31 March 1955

f. BIRD. *Dated* 31 March 1955

FAUN'S HEAD. *Dated* 28 June 1955
Plate. D. 10½

BOUQUET AND APPLE. *Dated* 22 January 1956
Plate. D. 10½

DANCERS. Easter 1956. Plaque. D. 10½

GOAT. Easter 1956. Plate. D. 10½

FISH. *Dated* 19 May 1956. Dish. D. 17

BATHERS. July 1956. Plaque. D. 7⅞

FAUN AND GOAT DANCING. July 1956
Plaque. D. 10½

DANCERS. July 1956. Plate. D. 10½

THREE BATHERS. August 1956
Dish with domed center. D. 12½. Moulded
biscuit dish painted in black slip by Picasso,
and glazed

63. BULL'S HEAD. *Dated* 23 November 1956
Plaque. D. 9¾

64. LARGE VASE WITH FISH. 1956
H. 18⅞. Red slip decoration

65. HEAD. Dish. D. 16⅞

66. TWO FACES. Vase. H. 14½

67. TWO FACES. Vase. H. 14½

68. CAVALIER. Dish. D. 17

69. CAVALIER AND FLUTIST. Dish. D. 14½

70. DANCING BACCHANTE AND FLUTE PLAYER.
Dish. D. 13

71. FACE AND HANDS. Dish. D. 17

72. FACE WITH IVY LEAVES. Dish. D. 17

73. RED AND WHITE OWL. *Dated* 22 February 1953
Painted terra cotta. H. 13¾
Nelson A. Rockefeller, New York

74. OWL. *Dated* 1953
Painted terra cotta. H. 13⅜
Philip L. Goodwin, New York

75. OWL JUG. c. 1953
White with black and brown slip. H. 22
Stedelijk Museum, Amsterdam

12, 14, 24. *Pigeons.*

1. *The Frugal Repast*, 1904.

15. *Bust of Young Woman*, 1906.

9. *Acrobats with Baboon*, 1905.

Catalogue
of the Prints

40. *Young Sculptor at Work*, 1933.

the interest of brevity the following identifications have been adopted:
MA for Philadelphia Museum of Art; NGA *Rosenwald Collection* to
dicate prints lent by the National Gallery of Art, all of which are from
Lessing J. Rosenwald Collection; G. followed by number refers to
rnhard Geiser, *Picasso, Peintre-Graveur*, Berne, 1933; M. followed by
mber refers to Fernand Mourlot, *Picasso Lithographe*, Monte Carlo,
49-56, 3 vols.; B. followed by number refers to Hans Bolliger, *Picasso*
Vollard, New York, 1956.

1. THE FRUGAL REPAST. 1904. Etching, G. 2, IIa,
   before Vollard edition. Art Institute of Chicago,
   Alfred Stieglitz Collection

2. WOMAN'S HEAD. 1905. Etching, G. 3a, before
   Vollard edition. PMA

3. THE POOR. 1905. Etching, G. 4, IIb, Vollard
   edition. PMA

4. TWO ACROBATS. *Dated* 1905. Drypoint, G. 6a,
   before Vollard edition. Louis E. Stern, New
   York

5. WOMAN'S PROFILE. 1905. Drypoint, G. 7b, Vollard edition. Museum of Modern Art, Lillie P.
   Bliss Collection

6. THE ACROBATS. *Dated* 1905. Drypoint, G. 9b,
   Vollard edition. PMA, Arensberg Collection

7. THE WATERING PLACE. 1905. Drypoint, G. 10a,
   before Vollard edition, signed in ink. NGA,
   Rosenwald Collection

8. AT THE CIRCUS. 1905. Drypoint, G. 11b, Vollard edition. PMA, Gallatin Collection

9. ACROBATS WITH BABOON. *Dated* 1905. Drypoint,
   G. 13a, before Vollard edition. NGA, Rosenwald
   Collection

10. THE BATH. *Dated* 1905. Drypoint, G. 14b, Vol-
    lard edition. Louis E. Stern, New York

11. LA TOILETTE DE LA MÈRE. 1905. Etching,
    G. 15b, Vollard edition, signed in pencil. PMA

12. SALOMÉ. *Dated* 1905. Drypoint, G. 17b, Vollard
    edition. PMA, Curt Valentin Bequest

13. THE DANCE. 1905. Drypoint, G. 18b, Vollard
    edition. PMA, gift of George Sharp Munson

14. BUST OF WOMAN. 1905-06. Woodcut, G. 211.
    NGA, Rosenwald Collection

15. BUST OF YOUNG WOMAN. 1906. Woodcut,
    G. 212, from 1933 edition of 15 printed and
    signed by Picasso. NGA, Rosenwald Collection

16. TWO NUDES. 1909. Drypoint, G. 21. PMA Arens-
    berg Collection

17. STILL LIFE WITH COMPOTE. 1909. Drypoint,
    G. 22. PMA

18. MAN'S HEAD. 1912. Etching, G. 32. PMA

19. STILL LIFE WITH BOTTLE. 1912. Drypoint,
    G. 33. PMA, Arensberg Collection

20. MAN WITH GUITAR. 1915. Engraving, G. 51.
    NGA, Rosenwald Collection

21. LA SOURCE. 1921. Drypoint and engraving,
    G. 61. PMA, Print Club Permanent Collection

22. THREE WOMEN. 1922-23. Drypoint and aqua-
    tint, G. 102. PMA

23. LA TOILETTE. 1923. Lithograph, G. 235, M. xv.
    PMA, Print Club Permanent Collection

24. WOMAN BY THE SEA. 1924. Lithograph, G. 237,
    M. xvii. NGA, Rosenwald Collection

25. WOMAN ON COUCH. 1924. Lithograph, G. 238,
    M. xviii. PMA, Gallatin Collection

26. WOMAN'S HEAD. 1925. Lithograph, G. 240,
    M. xx. PMA

76. *Minotauromachia,* 1935.

). *Dated* 7 April 1933. B. 68

). *Dated* 11 April 1933. B. 70

. *Dated* 3 May 1933. B. 71

?. *Dated* 3 May 1933. B. 72

3. *Dated* 4 May 1933. B. 74

-. *Dated* 5 May 1933. B. 75

5. *Dated* 5 May 1933. B. 76

5. *Dated* 29 January 1934. B. 79

7. *Dated* 2 March 1934. B. 81

3. *Dated* 10 March 1934. B. 82

s. 59-64—Etchings from 1933 *Minotaur* Series, ntified by date and Bolliger number.

). *Dated* 17 May 1933. B. 83

). *Dated* 18 May 1933. B. 86

. *Dated* 29 May 1933. B. 89

?. *Dated* 30 May 1933. B. 90

3. *Dated* 18 June 1933. B. 92

4. *Dated* 18 June 1933. Drypoint, B. 93

5. ACROBATS WITH A HORSE. *Dated* 11 November 1933. Drypoint, B. 17

5. FLUTE PLAYER AND GIRL WITH TAMBOURINE. *Dated* 30 January 1934. Etching, B. 20

7. TWO NUDES AND REMBRANDT PORTRAIT. *Dated* 31 January 1934. Etching, B. 35

3. STANDING NUDE AND REMBRANDT PORTRAIT. *Dated* 31 January 1934. Etching, B. 36

). BULL, HORSE, AND WOMAN. *Dated* 20 June 1934. Etching and engraving, B. 22

). TAUROMACHY. *Dated* 8 September 1934. Etching. Museum of Modern Art, acquired through Lillie P. Bliss Bequest

1. SPHINX WITH BULL'S HEAD. c. 1934. Etching and engraving, B. 13

s. 72-75—*Blind Minotaur* Series 1934-35, identi-1 by date and Bolliger number.

?. *Dated* 22 September 1934. Etching and engraving, B. 94

3. *Dated* 23 October 1934. Etching, B. 96

4. c. 1934. Etching and engraving, B. 95

5. c. 1935. Etching and aquatint, B. 97

5. MINOTAUROMACHIA. 1935. Etching. PMA, gift of Henry P. McIlhenny

77. FORMS. 1935. Etching and aquatint, PMA

78. BOY AND SLEEPING WOMAN. c. 1935. Etching and aquatint, B. 26

79. HARPY AND THREE MYTHOLOGICAL FIGURES. c. 1935. Etching and aquatint, B. 24

80. SATYR AND SLEEPING WOMAN. 1936. Etching and aquatint, B. 27

81. THE DREAM AND LIE OF FRANCO. *Dated* January 1937. Etching and aquatint. PMA

82. COMBAT. *Dated* 10 October 1937. Engraving and etching. NGA, Rosenwald Collection

83. PORTRAIT OF VOLLARD. 1937. Etching, B. 100. NGA, Rosenwald Collection

84. DANCER WITH TAMBOURINE. 1938. Etching and aquatint. PMA, Curt Valentin Bequest

85. WOMAN'S HEAD. 1938. Engraving from the portfolio *Solidarité*. Louis E. Stern, New York

86. WOMAN'S HEAD. 1945. Lithograph, M. 1. PMA

87. BOY'S HEAD. *Dated* 7 November 1945. Lithograph, M. 8. Museum of Modern Art, Curt Valentin Bequest

88. YOUNG GIRL. 1945. Lithograph, M. 12 final state. PMA, Curt Valentin Bequest

84. *Dancer with Tambourine*, 1938.

89. *The Bull*, 1945-46.

5. *Bullfight Game*, 1954.

01. WOMAN IN ARMCHAIR. *Dated* 16 February 1947.
Color lithograph, M. 69. Museum of Modern Art

02. COMPOSITION WITH VASE OF FLOWERS. *Dated* 10
March 1947. Color lithograph, M. 74. Museum
of Modern Art, gift of Victor F. Riesenfeld

03. THE SLEEPER. *Dated* 23 March 1947. Lithograph, M. 81. Museum of Modern Art

04. YOUNG WOMAN'S HEAD. *Dated* 24 June 1947.
Lithograph, M. 106. NGA, Rosenwald Collection

05. DAVID AND BATHSHEBA (after Cranach). 1947.
Lithograph, M. 109 iv/x. PMA, Curt Valentin
Bequest

06. LARGE OWL. 1948. Lithograph, M. 110. Weyhe
Gallery, New York

07. FAUN MUSICIAN III. 1948. Lithograph, M. 114.
Weyhe Gallery, New York

08. FAUN'S HEAD (from the Second Vallauris Poster).
1948. Color lithograph, M. 119 ter.
Weyhe Gallery, New York

129. *The Little Artist*, 1954.

109. *Dancing Centaur*, 1948.

109. DANCING CENTAUR. 1948. Lithograph, M. 121. PMA, Curt Valentin Bequest

110. BULL'S HEAD. 1948. Lithograph, M. 123. PMA, gift of Henry P. McIlhenny

111. BLACK FIGURE. 1948. Lithograph, M. 126. PMA, Curt Valentin Bequest

112. DOVE. 1949. Lithograph, M. 141. PMA, gift of Philadelphia Water Color Club

113. LOBSTER. 1949. Lithograph, M. 143. PMA

114. TOAD. *Dated* 13 January 1949. Lithograph, M. 144. Museum of Modern Art, Mrs. John D. Rockefeller, Jr., Purchase Fund

115. BUST WITH STARRY BACKGROUND. *Dated* 7 April 1949. Lithograph, M. 163. PMA, Curt Valentin Bequest

116. PICADOR. *Dated* 11-15 March 1949. Lithograph, M. 172. PMA, gift of Henry P. McIlhenny

117. WOMAN WITH HAIR NET. *Dated* 28 March, 18 April, 30 May 1949. Color lithograph, M. 178 ter. PMA, Curt Valentin Bequest

118. DEPARTURE. *Dated* 20 May 1951. Color lithograph, M. 201. Museum of Modern Art, Mrs. John D. Rockefeller, Jr., Purchase Fund

119. GIRL AT WINDOW. 1952. Aquatint. PMA, Curt Valentin Bequest

120. GOAT'S HEAD. *Dated* 14 May 1952. Aquatint. NGA, Rosenwald Collection

121. HEN. *Dated* 23 June 1952. Aquatint. PMA, Curt Valentin Bequest

122. PALOMA AND DOLL. *Dated* 14 December 195 Lithograph, M. 229. Museum of Modern A Curt Valentin Bequest

123. WOMAN'S HEAD. *Dated* 4 January 1953. Lith graph, M. 232. Weyhe Gallery, New York

124. MOTHER AND CHILDREN. *Dated* 20 January 195 Lithograph, M. 239. PMA

125. BULLFIGHT GAME. *Dated* 14 February 195 Lithograph, M. 247. PMA, Curt Valentin Bequest

126. DANCE OF THE BANDERILLAS. *Dated* 14 Februa 1954. Lithograph, M. 248. Museum of Mode Art, Larry Aldrich Fund

127. THE CLOTHED MODEL. *Dated* 19 and 26 Marc 1954. Lithograph, M. 257. Museum of Modern Art

128. THE OLD PAINTER'S STUDIO. *Dated* 14 Marc 1954. Color lithograph, M. 260. Museum Modern Art, Curt Valentin Bequest

129. THE LITTLE ARTIST. *Dated* 18 May 1954. Col lithograph, M. 263. NGA, Rosenwald Collectic

130. TWO CLOWNS. *Dated* 28 March 1954. Col lithograph, M. 264. Museum of Modern Art, Curt Valentin Bequest

Catalogue of the Books

Louis E. Stern has lent from his comprehensive collection the following group of books containing original prints by Picasso. Catalogue references are thus abbreviated: Mat. followed by number refers to H. Matarasso, *Bibliographie des livres illustrés par Pablo Picasso. Oeuvres graphiques—1905-1956*, Nice, 1956; G. followed by number refers to Bernhard Geiser, *Picasso, Peintre-Graveur*, Berne, 1933; M. followed by number refers to Fernand Mourlot, *Picasso, Lithographe*, Monte Carlo, 1949-1956, 3 vols.

1. SAINT MATOREL by Max Jacob. Paris, Henry Kahnweiler, 1911. Mat. 2. Edition: 106. 4 etchings, G. 23-26.
2. LE SIÈGE DE JÉRUSALEM by Max Jacob. Paris, Henry Kahnweiler, 1914. Mat. 3. Edition: 106. 3 etchings and drypoints, G. 35-37.
3. LE TRICORNE. Album du Ballet Russe. Paris, Editions Paul Rosenberg, 1920. Mat. 8. 1 etching, G. 56, appearing only in 50 ed. de luxe.
4. LA JEUNE PARQUE by Paul Valéry. Paris, Nouvelle Revue Française, 1921. Mat. 9. Edition: 525. 1 lithograph, G. 244, M. IV.
5. CRAVATES DE CHANVRE by Pierre Reverdy. Paris, Editions Nord-Sud, 1922. Mat. 10. Edition: 132 (of which 30 special copies have 2 extra etchings, G. 64-65). 1 etching, G. 63.
6. CLAIR DE TERRE by André Breton. Paris, (Breton), 1923. Mat. 11. 1 drypoint, G. 110, appearing only in 40 ed. de luxe.
7. PICASSO. OEUVRES 1920-1926 by Christian Zervos. Paris, Editions Cahiers d'Art, 1926. Mat 13. 1 etching, G. 99, appearing only in 56 ed. de luxe.
8. PICASSO DESSINS by Waldemar George. Paris, Editions des Quatre Chemins, 1926. Mat. 14. 1 lithograph, G. 240, M. XX, appearing only in 100 ed. de luxe.
9. LE MANUSCRIT AUTOGRAPHE, No. 21. Paris, Auguste Blaizot et fils, May-June, 1929. Mat. 16. Edition: 300. 1 lithograph, G. 246, M. XXVI.

1. From *Saint Matorel* by Max Jacob

7. From *Picasso. Oeuvres* by Christian Zervos

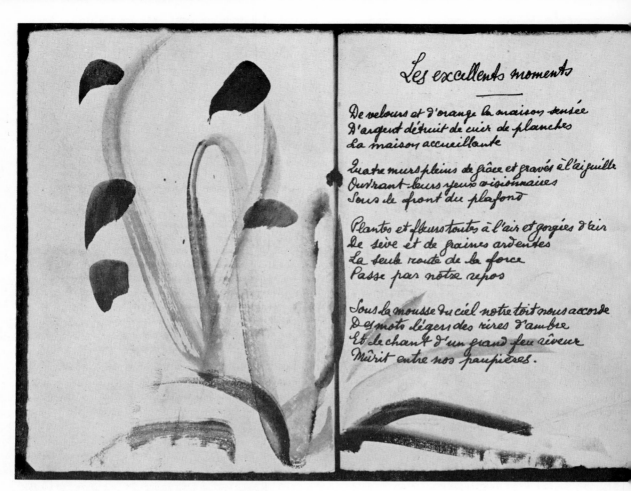

Les excellents moments

De velours et d'orange la maison sensée
D'argent détruit de cuir de planches
La maison accueillante

Quatre murs pleins de grâce et gravés à l'aiguille
Ouvrant leurs yeux visionnaires
Sous le front du plafond

Plantes et fleurs toutes à l'air et gorgées d'air
De sève et de graines ardentes
La seule route de la force
Passe par notre repos

Sous la mousse du ciel notre toit nous accorde
Des mots légers des rires d'ambre
Et le chant d'un grand feu rêveur
Mûrit entre nos paupières.

17. From *Divers Poèmes du Livre Ouvert* by Paul Eluard

16. From *Afat* by Iliazd

10. Le Chef-d'Oeuvre Inconnu by Balzac. Paris, Ambroise Vollard, 1931. Mat. 18. Edition: 340. 13 etchings, G. 123-135, and 67 drawings engraved in wood by Georges Aubert. An additional portfolio of 99 signed sets with *remarques* also appeared.

11. Les Métamorphoses by Ovid. Lausanne, Editions Albert Skira, 1931. Mat. 19. Edition: 145. 30 etchings, G. 143-172.

12. L'Antitête by Tristan Tzara. Paris, Les Cahiers Libres, 1933. Mat. 20. 1 etching appearing only in 18 ed. de luxe.

13. Lysistrata by Aristophanes. New York, The Limited Editions Club, 1934. Mat. 22. Edition: 1500. 6 etchings. There were also 150 extra sets of etchings, signed.

14. Sueño y Mentira de Franco by Picasso. Paris, 1937. Mat. 26. Edition: 850 regular and 150 signed on Japan. 2 aquatints.

15. Solidarité by Paul Eluard. Paris, G.L.M., 1938. Mat. 27. Edition: 150. 1 engraving by Picasso (see No. 85 of Print catalogue), as well as prints by other artists.

16. Afat by Iliazd (Ilya Zdanevitch). Paris, Le Degré Quarante et Un (Iliazd), 1940. Mat. 30. Edition 64. 4 etchings and engravings, and 2 aquatints.

17. Divers Poèmes du Livre Ouvert by Paul Eluard. Paris, (Eluard), 1941. Mat. 33. Edition: 15. 20 pages in manuscript by Eluard, and each decorated in water colors by Picasso.

18. Histoire Naturelle by Buffon. Paris, Martin Fabiani, 1942. Mat. 34. Edition: 226. 31 etchings and lift-ground aquatints.

19. Non-Vouloir by Georges Hugnet. Paris, Editions Jeanne Bucher, 1942. Mat. 35. Edition: 430. This copy, dedicated to Eluard from Hugnet and containing Hugnet's manuscript of *Non-Vouloir*, written in red ink, is one of four undescribed copies on China paper containing 23 prints: 1 engraving printed 4 times in different colors; and 4 metal cuts, printed in relief 4 times each in different colors and superimposed upon each other in 3 different combinations.

20. La Chèvre-Feuille by Georges Hugnet. Paris, Robert J. Godet, 1943. Mat. 36. 6 hand-etched photo-engravings printed in relief. In 42 special copies (including 8 "secret" sets on *vélin rouge*, of which this is one) there is an extra set of illustrations printed in 3 colors and a proof of 1 of the photo-engravings, printed as an intaglio plate.

10. From *Le Chef-d'Oeuvre Inconnu* by Balzac

21. CONTRÉE by Robert Desnos. Paris, Robert J. Godet, 1944. Mat. 37. Edition: 213. 1 etching. Inserted is a special proof of the etching decorated and signed by the artist.

22. A PABLO PICASSO by Paul Eluard. Geneva, Editions de Trois Collines, 1944. Mat. 38. Edition: 90. 1 etching.

23. LE MARTEAU SANS MAÎTRE by René Char. Paris, Librairie José Corti, 1945. Mat. 40. 1 etching appearing only in 25 ed. de luxe.

24. DOS CONTES by Ramon Reventos. Paris-Barcelona, Editorial Albor, 1947. Mat. 41. Edition: 250. 4 etchings.

25. DEUX CONTES by Ramon Reventos. Paris, Editions Albor, 1947. Mat. 42. Edition: 250. 4 drypoints.

26. DU CUBISME by A. Gleizes and J. Metzinger. Paris, Compagnie Française des Arts Graphiques, 1947. Mat. 43. Edition: 455. 1 etching, G. 42, by Picasso as well as prints by other artists.

27. CINQ SONNETS by Petrarch. Paris, A la Fontaine de Vaucluse, 1947. Mat. 44. Edition: 110. 1 etching.

28. VINGT POÈMES by Gongora. Paris, Les Grands Peintres Modernes et le Livre, 1948. Mat. 45. Edition: 275. 41 drypoints and lift-ground aquatints.

29. ESCRITO by Iliazd (Ilya Zdanevitch). Paris, Latitud cuarenta y uno (Iliazd), 1948. Mat. 46. Edition: 66. 6 etchings and drypoints.

30. LE CHANT DES MORTS by Pierre Reverdy. Paris, Tériade, 1948. Mat. 47. Edition: 270. 125 lithographs, M. 117.

31. ELÉGIE D'IHPÉTONGA by Yvan Goll. Paris, Editions Hémisphères, 1949. Mat. 49. Edition: 220. 4 lithographs, M. 177, extra set on Japan in 20 special copies.

32. POÉSIE DE MOTS INCONNUS edited by Iliazd (Ilya Zdanevitch). Paris, Le Degré 41 (Iliazd), 1949. Mat. 50. Edition: 171. 1 engraving and 2 lithographs, M. 181, by Picasso as well as prints by other artists.

33. CARMEN by Prosper Mérimée. Paris, La Bibliothèque Française, 1949. Mat. 51. Edition: 320. 38 engravings (plus 4 extra aquatints in 11 ed. de luxe).

34. PICASSO LITHOGRAPHE (Vol. I, 1919-1947) by Fernand Mourlot. Monte Carlo, André Sauret, 1949. Mat. 52. Edition: 2500. 2 lithographs, M. 160 and 174.

35. PICASSO LITHOGRAPHE (Vol. II, 1947-1949) by Fernand Mourlot. Monte Carlo, André Sauret, 1950. Mat. 53. Edition: 2005 for cover, 2010 for frontispiece. 2 lithographs, M. 186 and 98.

36. CORPS PERDU by Aimé Césaire. Paris, Editions Fragrance, 1950. Mat. 54. Edition: 219. 32 etchings and engravings.

37. L'AGE DE SOLEIL by Robert J. Godet. Paris, (Godet), 1950. Mat. 55. 1 etching printed twice (in intaglio and again in relief) and 1 drypoint entitled "La Torera," appearing only in 114 ed. de luxe.

38. DE MÉMOIRE D'HOMME by Tristan Tzara. Paris, Bordas éditeur, 1950. Mat. 56. Edition: 350. 9 lithographs, M. 187.

39. LE VISAGE DE LA PAIX by Paul Eluard. Paris, Editions Cercle d'Art, 1951. Mat. 57. 1 lithograph, M. 203, appearing only in 150 ed. de luxe.

40. DONS DES FÉMININES by Valentine Penrose. Paris, Librairie "Les Pas Perdus," 1951. Mat. 58. 1 drypoint appearing only in 50 ed. de luxe. In this copy 2 extra prints of same subject in different colors have been inserted.

41. LA MAIGRE by Adrian de Monluc. Paris, Le Degré Quarante et Un (Iliazd), 1952. Mat. 59. Edition: 74 (also four additional sets of plates). 10 drypoints.

42. LA CHÈVRE by André Verdet. Paris, Editions de Beaune, 1952. Mat. 61. 1 aquatint appearing only in 50 ed. de luxe.

43. SIX CONTES FANTASQUES by Maurice Toesca. Paris, Flammarion, 1953. Mat. 62. Edition: 255, including 30 sets of the engravings and drypoints alone. 6 engravings and drypoints.

44. LA GUERRE ET LA PAIX by Claude Roy. Paris, Editions Cercle d'Art, 1954. Mat. 63. 1 lithograph, M. 245, appearing only in 100 ed. de luxe.

45. LE BALLET by Boris Kochno. Paris, Editions du Monde, Hachette, 1954. Mat. 64. Edition: 1055. 1 color lithograph, M. 259.

46. POÈMES ET LITHOGRAPHIES by Picasso. Paris, Galerie Louise Leiris, 1954. Mat. 65. Edition: 52. 14 lithographs, M. 180.

47. A HAUTE FLAMME by Tristan Tzara. Paris, 1955. Mat. 66. Edition: 70. 6 engravings.

48. Hélène Chez Archimède by André Suarez. Paris, Nouveau Cercle Parisien du Livre, 1955. Mat. 67. Edition: 240. 22 wood-engravings by Georges Aubert after Picasso.

49. Picasso Dessins d'un Demi-Siècle. Paris, Berggruen & Cie., 1956. Mat. 68. Edition: 1,000. 1 lithograph, M. 268.

50. Chevaux de Minuit by Robert Grey. Paris, Iliazd, 1956. Mat. 69. Edition: 68. 12 drypoints and engravings.

51. Nuit by René Crevel. Alès, P. A. Benoît, 1956. Mat. 70. Edition: 30. 1 etching.

52. Chronique des Temps Héroiques by Max Jacob. Paris, Louis Broder, 1956. Mat. 71. Edition: 170. 3 lithographs, 3 drypoints, and 24 wood-engravings after drawings.

53. Un Poème dans Chaque Livre by Paul Eluard. Paris, Louis Broder, 1956. Mat. 72. Edition: 120. 2 drypoints by Picasso as well as prints by other artists.

54. Picasso Lithographe (Vol. III, 1949-1956) by Fernand Mourlot. Monte Carlo, André Sauret, 1956. Mat. 73. Edition size unknown. 2 lithographs.

55. Picasso: Peintures, Dessins, Gravures Rares by Gilberte Duclaud. Cannes, Galerie 65, 1956. (Not in Mat.) Edition size unknown. 1 color lithograph on cover (50 copies were printed separately and signed by the artist).

56. Picasso Derrière le Masque by P. A. Benoît. Alès, (Benoît), 1957. Mat. 74. Edition: 36. 1 engraving.

57. 40 Dessins en Marge du Buffon by Picasso. Paris, Jonquières, 1957. (Not in Mat.) 1 metal cut printed in relief appearing only in 226 ed. de luxe.

58. Témoignage by Jean Cocteau. Paris, Pierre Bertrand, 1957. (Not in Mat.) Edition: 125. 1 etching by Picasso, and 1 engraved portrait of Picasso by Paul Lemagny.

59. Autre Chose Que de l'Enfant Beau by Antonin Artaud. Paris, Louis Broder, 1957. (Not in Mat.) Edition: 120. 1 color drypoint.

60. Picasso Peintures 1955-1956. Paris, Galerie Louise Leiris, 1957. (Not in Mat.) Edition size unknown. 1 color lithograph on cover.

From *Histoire Naturelle* by Buffon

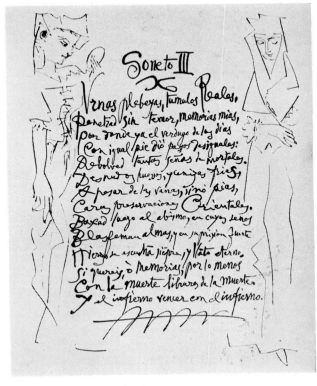

28. From *Vingt Poèmes* by Gongora

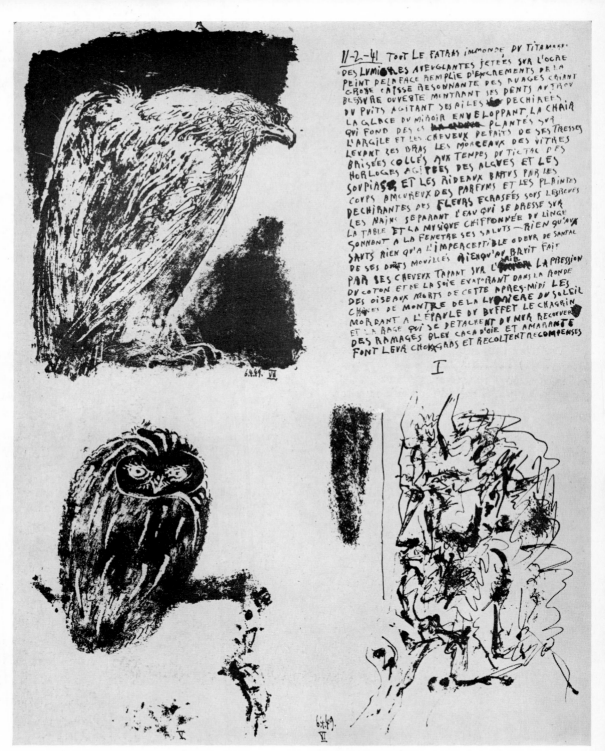

46. From *Poèmes et Lithographies* by Picasso